Cold War Fighter Pilot Songbook

The compilation of the book contains not all the songs they sung during the Cold War era, but quiet a lot. The sources were exclusively my collection of unpublished Squadron Songbooks throughout the english speaking Fighter Pilots Community. They reflect the sheer emotions, the black humors of ill fated conflicts and the absence of women during their deployments. At the time the compilation is published, most of the songs are already banned from the Squadrons and O-Clubs and within short time they will be forgotten as a Social Squadron Part of a special Breed of Aviators during the 70s trough 90s.
Joseph F. Tuso wrote in his book "Singing the Vietnam Blues", 1990, in his "Overture": "... Fellowship, love, hate, joy, loneliness. even despair – these are all found in the songs in this collection. I do not delude myself that these are great songs, but they are truthful songs, they are historic songs, and the deserve to be preserved. By some people, they will even be cherished."

Thirty years later, I have nothing to add to the words of Major Tuso.

"Fortuna" flew fighter-bomber aircraft and was an instructor pilot for almost ten years. He collected "Fighter Pilot Songs" as recordings (CD, Tapes), and the respective songbooks throughout his flying career.

Cold War Fighter Pilots Songbook

Call Sign: Fortuna

All pictures by "Fortuna"

First and only Edition 2024

Email: check-six@gmx.de

ISBN: 978-37583053-3-7

Production and publishing:
BoD - Books on Demand, Norderstedt

Old and new Fighter Pilot Songs

A Night With The Fighter Pilots at the (O-) Club

Collection Period
1975 – 2005

Not all pilots flying fighter aircraft are "Fighter Pilots",
and some "Fighter Pilots" are not flying fighter aircraft,
some are even not in the Air Force!

Introduction

In 1976 I earned my "Wings" in the Undergraduate Pilot Training at Sheppard AFB, Texas. It was the very first time I heard the songs sung in the "Duffys Pilot's Bar", especially on friday nights, when a week of "Flying Business" was done, or on special occasions, for a "After Night Flight Beer", Birthdays or Squadron's festivities.

The first songs at night at the bar were mostly one of the classical songs, which have their roots in the WW II, Korea- or Vietnam War. I included 13 lyrics of the old classical songs. If You are searching for more classical lyrics, check the Sources.

After some more beers, the songs changed into the "Dirty Ditties" and the "Bawdy Ballads". 79 new Fighter Pilot Songs and 201 Dirty Ditties out of the unpublished SQN songbooks are found in my compilation.

Within the Cold War era, the pilots have sung and modified these songs. The lyrics got more definite, more offensive. To be honest, the more voluptuous the society became in those days, the more distinct some lyrics were. But nevertheless, these are the songs, Fighter Pilots were singing during the Cold War era, on special occasions.

Within the NATO, all Air Forces train, fly and fight together. And after the work is done, there are some opportunities to drink and to sing together, too. Because the mutual language while flying, talking and singing is English, there are mostly Anglo-Saxon "Fighter Pilots Songs", sung by Pilots in their squadrons or at the bar in the Officers-Clubs, on Festivities, Squadron exchanges, or just after Nightflight, having a "Nightflight-Beer" in the Squadron lounge.

Therefore, there are only a few typical French, Italian or German Air Force Songs around.

Exceptions are for a few German drinking songs, which are also well known to the British and US Pilots, having been stationed in Germany or having participated in NATO exercises.

Quiet a few of the songs have been submitted to my collection. Thank You to all of You Fighter Pilots pals, worldwide.

All songs compiled in this book, derive from "Squadron-, Wing- or Combat Songbooks".

The bibliography at the end of the book lists the unpublished songbooks of my collection. The authors of the lyrics are often unknown, except for some very common songs e.g. by Dick Jonas or Toby Hughes.

Political correctness has changed.
And it is good, that it has changed!
But not preserving the lyrics, which were sung and boosted the spirit, would neglect the history of some or many pilots, for sure not all of them, who flew combat aircrafts during the Cold War and in combat.

Additionally, don't blame me for the words, grammer and slang of the lyrics, I just collected the songbooks as they were covertly handled and spread below the tables.

Check Six!

Fortuna

The Hymnal

WARNING[1]

The material contained in this compilation does not necessarily reflect the thoughts or opinions of the author, his employer, or humanity at large. Contents are subject to change without notice. Any resemblance to actual persons, living or dead, is unintentional and wholly coincidental. Use of the masculine pronoun is intended to include both genders where appropriate. Contents slightly enlarged to show detail. Hand wash only, drip dry. Do not bend, fold, mutilate, or spindle. Anchovies or jalapeños added upon request. Actual mileage may vary. No substitutions allowed. No deposit, no return. For a limited time only, quantities limited while supplies last, at participating locations only. This offer void where prohibited. Songs provided "as is" without any warranties expressed or implied. User assumes full liabilities. An equal opportunity song collector. No shoes, no shirt, no songs. Don't pee in my songbook and I won't sing in your bathroom. Caveat emptor. Use at your own risk. Parental advisory: explicit lyrics; text contains material some readers may find objectionable. Adult themes. Childish themes. Themes that make little or no sense. Keep away from small children, household pets, and D. F. Limit one per customer. No money down, no purchase required, variable APR as low as 12.9%. You need not be present to win. Some assembly required. Batteries not included. Action figures sold separately; collect them all! No preservatives added.

---

[1] TLP Songbook / CD.

Contents may settle during shipping. *Pre-cooked weight. Sealed for your protection. Do not use if safety seal is broken. Refrigerate after opening. Safety goggles required during use. If pregnant, please consult your physician prior to use. For external use only. If rash, redness, irritation, or swelling develops, *immediately* discontinue use; if symptoms persist, consult a doctor. Avoid extreme temperatures and store in a cool dry place. Keep away from open flames. Do not place near flammable or magnetic source. Avoid inhaling fumes or contact with mucous membranes. Smoking contents may be hazardous to your health. This book produced from 100% recycled electrons and particles of inanimate matter. No live animals were used to test the offensiveness of the contents.

Contents may be hot! Contains 100% of the recommended daily allowance of seven essential vitamins and minerals. No salt, MSG, artificial color or flavor added. Contents are ribbed for your pleasure. Slippery when wet. Must be 18 to enter. Possible penalties for early withdrawal. One size fits all. Offer valid only at participating locations. State and local taxes may apply. Allow four to six weeks for delivery. This disclaimer does not cover tornado, flood, hurricane, lightning, earthquake, and other Acts of God; acts of war, declared or undeclared, including insurgency, terrorism, civil disorder, or the discharge of a nuclear device, whether intentional or accidental; misuse, neglect, unauthorized repair, damage from improper scoring, typos, misspelled words, incorrect line voltage, missing or altered verses, sonic boom vibrations, off-key notes, electromagnetic radiation from outer space, or customer adjustments that are not covered in the instructions; and incidents owing to motor vehicle accidents, ship sinkings, airplane crashes, accidental file deletions, projectiles, or failure to carry the tune. Other restrictions may apply. The Surgeon General of the United States warns that while use of this and similar products has been shown to provide effective protection against sexually transmitted diseases, the only guaranteed safeguard remains abstinence. If the contents offend you, lighten up, get a fucking life, and move on.

Note: If you are so politically correct or so up-tight that you get upset at bad "Fighter Pilot Language", Fighter Pilot Jokes, bawdy lyrics, raunchy humor, sarcasm, gallows humor, crash humor etc. , or if you are new to flying and are scared stiff, then ...

you should close the book NOW ! ...

... and hand this book forward, to a "Real Fighter Pilot"!

In the booklet for the CD "A Night at the Bar with the Boys", recorded in Scotland in 1989, a famous USAF General stated:

Over the pyrenees, on the dusty road to Issus, manning the oars at Salamis, men sung. Those men were, and are today, Warriors. Their songs extolled the bodily functions, particularly those of women, and more often than not were of rigid middle digit genre, pointed at the powers above that got them into this mess in the first place. Their voices happily laughed at the "handsome young copper walking his beat", and roared out applause for the athletic prowess of Mary Ann Burns who "could do tricks that would give a man the shits". You must believe the Companions under Alexander sang derisively of Darius and his palace full of concubines. And so it went. The old songs lived on through the ages. Words changed, tunes were altered, all to fit the times, but the songs themselves are the bonding and often the softening agent giving identity and courage to those facing the uncertainties of tomorrow. Not all were bawdy. In the late of the night voices were sometimes raised asking if the sun would rise tomorrow, or quietly praising the next man to die.

So here you have the latest, sung by the present crop of fighter pilots, perhaps different in many ways, but right out of the pages of history, down to today, and on throughout the ages, as long as there's a battle to be fought and beer to be drunk. Thanks Guys![1]

---

[1]www.horntip.com/mp3/1980s/1989--2002_a_night_at_the_bar_with_the_boys_(CD)/index.htm

Rules Of The Air

- ✓ Every takeoff is optional. Every landing is mandatory.
- ✓ If you push the stick forward, the houses get bigger. If you pull the stick back, they get smaller. That is, unless you keep pulling the stick all the way back, then they get bigger again.
- ✓ Flying isn't dangerous. Crashing is what's dangerous.
- ✓ It's always better to be down here wishing you were up there than up there wishing you were down here.
- ✓ The ONLY time you have too much fuel is when you're on fire.
- ✓ The propeller is just a big fan in front of the plane used to keep the pilot cool. When it stops, you can actually watch the pilot start sweating.
- ✓ When in doubt, hold on to your altitude. No one has ever collided with the sky.
- ✓ A 'good' landing is one from which you can walk away. A 'great' landing is one after which they can use the plane again.
- ✓ Learn from the mistakes of others. You won't live long enough to make all of them yourself.
- ✓ You know you've landed with the wheels up if it takes full power to taxi to the ramp.
- ✓ The probability of survival is inversely proportional to the angle of arrival. Large angle of arrival, small probability of survival and vice versa.
- ✓ Never let an aircraft take you somewhere your brain didn't get to five minutes earlier.

- ✓ **Stay out of clouds. The silver lining everyone keeps talking about might be another airplane going in the opposite direction. Reliable sources also report that mountains have been known to hide out in clouds.**
- ✓ **Always try to keep the number of landings you make equal to the number of take offs you've made.**

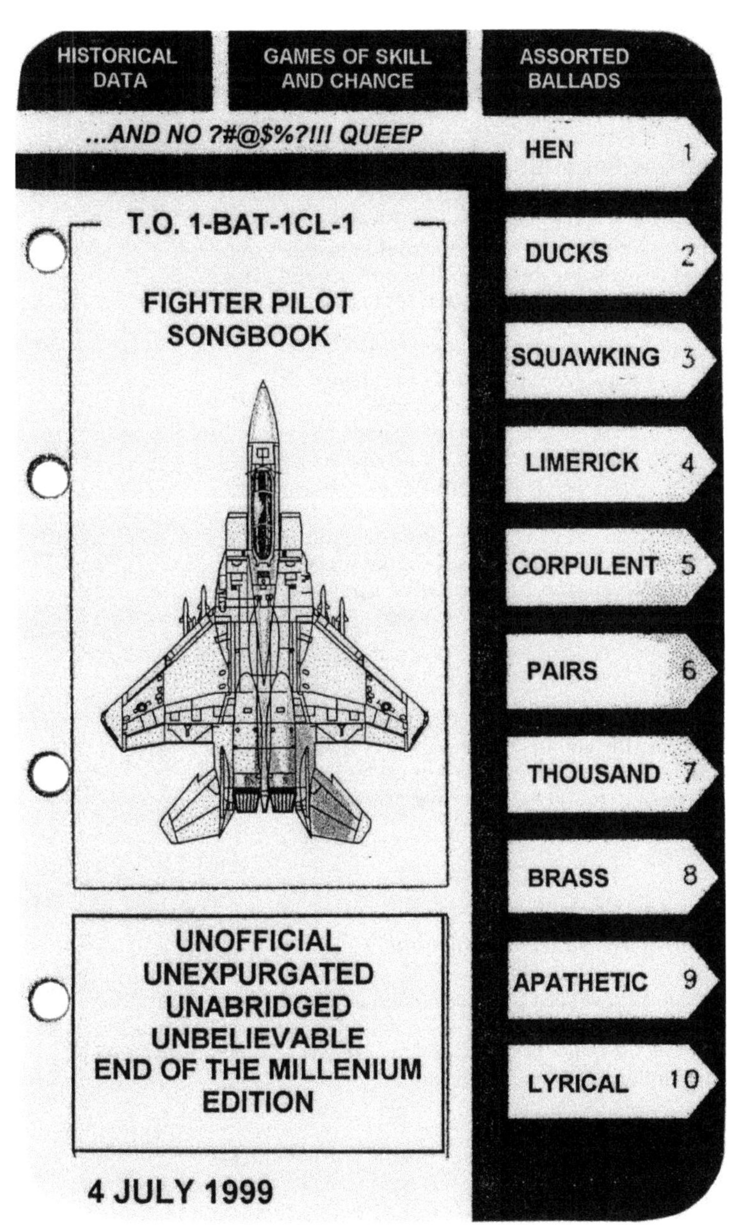

One of the many SQDN Songbooks

OLD CLASSICS

Adeline Schmidt

There was a young maiden named Adeline Schmidt
She went to a doctor 'cause she couldn't shit.
He gave her some medicine all wrapped up in glass
Up went the window and out went her ass!

Chorus:

> *It was brown, brown, shot all around*
> *Brown, brown, shit all around*
> *It was brown, brown, shit all around*
> *And the whole world was covered in*
> *SHIT-SHIT-SHIT-SHIT*

A handsome young copper was walking his beat.
He happened to be on that side of the street.
He looked up so bashful, he looked up so shy.
And a big piece of shit hit him right in the eye.

Chorus:

This handsome copper, he cussed and he swore.
He called the young maiden a dirty old whore.
And under a bridge you can still see him sit.
With a sign 'round his neck saying "blinded by shit."

Chorus:

The Air Force Lament
("Battle Hymn Of The Republic")

Mine eyes have seen the days of men who ruled the fighting sky,
With hearts that laughed at death and lived for nothing but to fly,
But now these hearts are grounded and those days are long gone by,
The Air Force is shot to hell.

Chorus:

> *Glorifying regulations, have them at every station.*
> *Burn the ass of those that break them, the Air Force is shot to hell.*

My bones have felt their pounding throb a hundred thousand strong,

A mighty airborne legion sent to right a deadly wrong,
But now it's only memory, it only lives in song,
The Air Force has gone to hell.
Chorus:

I have seen them in their T-bolts when their eyes were dancing flame,
I've seen their screaming power dives that blasted Goering's name,
But now they fly like sissies and hang their heads in shame,
Their spirit's shot to hell.
Chorus:

The Sabres in Korea drove the MiGs out of the sky,
The pilots were fearless men and not afraid to die,
But now the regs are written, you can kiss your ass goodbye,
The Air Force is shot to hell.
Chorus:

They flew their rugged Thunderchiefs through a living hell of flak,
And bloody, dying pilots gave their lives to bring them back,
But now they all play ping-pong in the operations shack,
Their techniques have gone to hell.
Chorus:

You heard the punding 50's blaze from wings of polished steel,
The purring of your Merlin was a song your heart could feel,
But now the O-2 charms you with its moanin', groanin' squeal,
And it will not climb for hell.
Chorus:

We were cocky, bold and happy when we played the angel's game,
We split the blue with buzzing and we rolled our way to fame,
But now that's all verboten and we're all so fucking tame,
Our spirit's shot to hell.
Chorus:

One day I buzzed an airfield with another reckless chap,
We flew a hot formation with his wingtip in my lap,
But there's a new directive and we'll have no more of that,
Or you will burn in hell.
Chorus:

Have you ever climbed a Lightning up to where the air is thin,
Have you stuck her long nose downward just to hear the screamin' din,
Have you tried to do it lately? Better not, you'll auger in,
And then you'll sure catch hell.

Chorus:
Mine eyes get dim with tears when I recall the days of old,
When pilots took their choice of being old or young and bold,
Alas, we have no choice and we'll live to be quite old,
The Air Force has gone to hell.
Chorus:

But smile awhile my pilot, though your eyes may still be wet,
Some day we'll meet in heaven where the rules have not been set,
And God will show us how to buzz and roll and really let,
The Air Force will fly like hell.

Final Chorus:
Glory no more regulations, rip them down at every station.
Ground the guy that tries to make one, and let us fly like hell!

Barnacle Bill The Sailor

Who's that knocking at my door?
Who's that knocking at my door?
Who's that knocking at my door?
Cried the fair young maiden.

It's only me from across the sea,
Said Barnacle Bill the sailor.

Why are you knocking at my door?
'Cos I'm young enough and ready and rough.

You can sleep upon the floor.
Oh get off the floor, you dirty old whore.

You can sleep upon the mat.
Oh bugger the mat, you can't fuck that.

You can sleep on the stairs.
Oh bugger the stairs they ain't got hairs.

You can sleep between my tits.
Oh bugger your tits, they give me the shits.

You can sleep between my thighs.
Oh bugger your thighs, they're covered with flies.
You can sleep within my cunt.

Oh bugger your cunt, but I'll fuck for a stunt.

What will we do when the baby's born?
Oh we'll drown the bugger and fuck for another.

Dear Mom

Of the 43rd Tactical Fighter Squadron, Vietnam

Dear Mom, your son is dead, he bought the farm today,
He crashed his OV-10 on the Ho Chi Minh highway.
He made a rocket pass, and then he busted his ass,
Hmm, hmm, hmmmmm.

He flew across the fence to see what he could see,
And there it was, as plain as it could be.
There was a truck on the road, with a big heavy load.
Hmm, hmm, hmmmmm.

He got right on the horn, and gave the DASC a call,
"Send me air, I've got a truck that's stalled."
The DASC said, "That's all right, I'll send the Stinger Flight,
For I AM THE POWER!"

Those Hornets checked right in, gunfighters two by two,
Low on gas and tanker overdue.
They asked the FAC to mark, just where the truck was parked,
Hmm, hmm, hmmmmm.

That Bronco rolled right in , with his smoke to mark,
Exactly where that fucking truck was parked
But now the rest is in doubt, 'cause he never pulled out,
Hmm, hmm, hmmmmm.

With reverence:
Dear Mom, your son is dead, he bought the farm today,
He crashed his OV-10 on the Ho Chi Minh Highway.
He made a rocket pass, then he busted his ass,
Hmm, hmm, hmmmmm.

Sung to "Camptown Races":
Motherfucker's dead, motherfucker's dead,
Son's comin' home in a body bag,
Oh, doo dah day!

Spoken:
How did he go? STRAIGHT IN!
What was he doing? THREE HUNDRED AND FIFTY-ONE!
Indicated? YEAH.

Cocksucker, motherfucker, eat a bag of shit,
Cunt hair, douche bag, bite your mother's tit.
We're the best fighter squadron, all the others suck.
Bronco FAC, Bronco FAC, rah, rah, FUCK!

I Don't Want To Join The Air Force

(Tune: Picadilly Underground)

I don't want to join the air force,
I don't want to go to war,
I'd rather hang around Picadilly Underground,
Living off the earnings of a high born lady.
Don't want a bullet up me asshole,
Don't want me buttocks shot away,
I'd rather stay in England,
Jolly, jolly England,
And fornicate my fucking life away!

Monday I touched her on the ankle,
Tuesday I touched her on the knee,
On Wednesday, I confess, I lifted up her dress,
Thursday I saw you-know-what,
Friday I put me hand upon it,
Saturday she gave me balls a tweak *(Tweak! Tweak!)*
And Sunday after supper, I put the old boy up 'er,
And now she earns me forty quid a week! Gor blimey.

Call out the Regimental Army,
Call out the Navy and Marines,
Call out me mother,
Me sister and me brother,
But for God's sake, don't call me, gor blimey.
I don't want a bayonet up me asshole,
I don't want me knackers shot away,
I'd rather live in England,
Merry, merry England,
And fornicate me fuckin' life away.

Mary Ann Burns

Mary Ann Burns is the queen of all acrobats
She can do tricks that would give a man the shits.
She can roll green peas off her fundamental orifice,
Do a double flip and catch them in her tits.
She's a great big son-of-a-bitch, oh, twice as big as me,
Hairs around her ass like branches on a tree.
She can swim, fish, fight, fuck, fly a plane, drive a truck,
Mary Ann Burns is the girl for me.

Red River Valley (Vietnam version)

To the Red River Valley we are going,
For to get us some trains and some trucks.
But if I had my say so about it,
I'd still be at home in the sack.

Come and sit by my side at the briefing,
Do not hasten to bid me adieu.
To the Red River Valley we're going,
And I'm flying four in Flight Blue.

We went for to check on the weather,
And they said it was clear as could be.
I lost my wingman 'round the field,
And the rest augured in out at sea.

Intel said there's no flak where we're going,
Intel said there's no flak on the way.
There's a dark overcast o'er the target,
I'm beginning to doubt what they say.

To the valley they say we are going,
And many strange sights will we see.
But the one there that held my attention,
Was the SAM that they threw up at me.

To the valley he said he was flying,
And he never saw the medal that he earned.
Many jocks have flown into the valley,
And a number have never returned.

So I listened as he briefed on the mission,
Tonight at the bar Teak Flight will sing.
But we're going to the Red River Valley,
And today you are flying my wing.

Oh, the flak is so thick in the valley,
That the MiGs and the SAMs we don't need.
So fly high and down-sun in the valley,
And guard well the ass of Teak Lead.

Now things turn to shit in the valley,
And the briefing I gave, you don't heed.
They'll be waiting at the Hanoi Hilton,
And it's fish heads and rice for Teak Lead.

We refueled on the way to the valley,
In the States it had always been fun.
But with thunder and lightning all around us,
Twas the last AAR for Teak One.

When he came to a bridge in the valley,
He saw a duty that he couldn't shun.
For the first to roll in on the target,
Was my leader, old Teak Number One.

Oh, he flew through the flak toward the target,
With his bombs and his rockets drew a bead.
But he never pulled out of his bomb run,
Twas fatal for another Teak Lead.

So come sit by my side at the briefing,
We will sit there and tickle the beads.
For we're going to the Red River Valley,
And my call sign for today is Teak Lead.

Stand To Your Glasses

We sit 'neath the resounding rafters,
The walls all around us are bare,
They echo back the laughter,
It seems that the dead are all here.

We climb in the purple twilight,
We loop in the silvery dawn,

With black smake trailing behind us,
To show where our comrades have gone.

Chorus:

We are the boys who fly high in the sky,
Bosom buddies while boozin' are we,
We are the boys that they send out to die,
Bosom buddies while boozin' are we.
Up in headquarters they scream and the shout,
'about lots of things they know nothing about
But we are the boys they send out to die,
Bosom buddies while boozin' are we.

Cut off from the land that bore us,
Betrayed by the land that we find;
The good men have all gone before us,
And only the dull left behind.

So stand by your glasses steady,
The world is a web of lies,
Here's to the dead already,
Hurrah for the next men to die.

Stand to your glasses steady
This world is a world full of lies
A toast to the dead already
Hurrah for the next man to die

Stand To Your Glasses (Vietnam Version, A.K.A "Bosom Buddies")

We fly in the purple twilight
We fly in the silvery dawn,
With smoke trails following after
To show where our comrades have gone.
So stand to your glasses ready
Don't let a tear leave your eye
Here's to the dead already
And hurrah for the next man to die.

Chorus:

We are the boys that they send out to fly,
Bosom buddies a-boozin' are we.
We are the boys that they send out to die,

Bosom buddies a-boozin' are we.

The fuck-heads at Seventh they scream and they shout,
They scream about things they know fuck-all about.

Swing Low, Sweet Chariot

Swing low, sweet chariot,
Coming for to carry me home,
Swing low, sweet chariot,
Coming for to carry me home.

I looked over Jordan, and what did I see,
Coming for to carry me home.
A band of angels, coming after me,
Coming for to carry me home.

The Copilot

I am a copilot, I sit on the right
I'm quick and courageous; I'm wonderfully bright
My job is remembering what the captain forgets
And I never talk back, so I have no regrets.

Chorus:

I'm a lousy copilot and a long way from home.

I make out the flight plan and study the weather,
Pull up the gear, drop it, and stand by to feather
I make out his mail forms, I hire his whores,
And I fly his old crate to the tune of his snores.

I make out the flight plan according to Hoyle
I take all the readings, I check on the oil,
I hustle him out for the midnight alarm
I fly through the fog while he sleeps on my arm.

I treat him to coffee, I keep him in cokes
I laugh at his corn and his horrible jokes
And once in a while, when his landings are rusty,
I come through with, "Yessiree captain,it's gusty!"

All in all, I'm commissioned a general stooge
I sit on the right of this high-flying Scrooge

Some day I'll make captain, and then I'll be blest,
I'll give my poor tongue one long hell of a rest.

There are No Fighter Pilots own In Hell

(Tune: If You Wanna Go to Heaven Clap Your Hands)

There are no fighter pilots down in hell,
There are no fighter pilots down in hell,
The place is full of queers, navigators, bombardiers,
There are no fighter pilots down in hell.

There are no fighter pilots in the States,
There are no fighter pilots in the States,
They're off on foreign shores, making mothers out of whores,
There are no fighter pilots in the States.

There are no fighter pilots up in wing,
There are no fighter pilots up in wing,
The place is full of brass, sitting 'round on their fat ass,
There are no fighter pilots up in wing.

A bomber pilot never takes a dare,
A bomber pilot never takes a dare,
The autopilot on, he's reading novels in the john,
A bomber pilot never takes a dare.

There are no bomber pilots in the fray,
There are no bomber pilots in the fray,
They are all in USOs, wearing womens' fancy clothes,
There are no bomber pilots in the fray.

It's naughty, naughty, naughty, but it's nice,
If you ever do it once you'll do it twice,
It'll wreck your reputation, but increase the population,
It's naughty, naughty, naughty, but it's nice.

YANKEE AIR PIRATES
OUR MIGHT ALWAYS
SONGS
TO DRINK B
Courtesy of PACAF'S PRIDE
TAKHLI RTAFB, THAILAND
355 TFW

35 TAC FTR WG
SONG BOOK

NEW FIGHTER PILOT SONGS

12 Days of Crisis

Tune: 12 Days of Christmas

On the first day of crisis the Execs gave to me,
A ticket to Saudi.

2nd day	2 bone domes
3rd day	3 wheels a flapping
4th day	1 Manston recce
5th day	5 PLJ's
6th day	6 pairs of long johns (never issued)
7th day	7 life-ex canisters
8th day	8 different handouts
9th day	The Blackie book of dodges
10th day	10 indecisions
11th day	11 evening briefings
12th day	Sweet FA

230 Organization

Tune: Capri, Capri the Isle of Capri

Now 230 Sqn's a mighty fine place,
But the organization's a fucking disgrace.
Thre's Execs and weehls and spaceman too,
Who sit on their arses with fuck all too do.
They sit on their arses, they scream and they shout.
They talk about things they know fuck all about.
And as for the good, they might just as well be-
Shoveling sand down in Saudi,
In Saudi, in Saudi,
Shoveling sand down in Saudi.

Now Al Jabayl airfield is a mighty fine place,
But it looks like the boys have got eggs on their face-
We still have no aircraft, we still have no maps,
We're given more injections and force-fed with Naps.
Now the Naps give us squirts and jabs hurt our arm,
But the doctor assures us they'll do us no harm.
By the end of the week we were all on our backs,
with pneumonic plague, Whooping cough and Anthrax.
On our backs, on our backs,
Flat on our backs with a dose of Anthrax.

322 Is In The Bar Tonight

322 is in the Bar tonight a little bit pissed and a bit tight.
322 is in the Bar tonight and the CO says it's gonna be alright.

Next verse same as first, a little louder and a little bit worse.
(Start very quiet, get louder & louder each new verse until U scream)

322 SUPERSTARS

3-2-2 Superstars, we are even better
than we think we are !!!
3-2-2 Superstars, we are even better
than we think we are !!!

79 Tage Krieg

79 Tage Krieg ließen nur Platz für einen Sieger,
SAM-Controller gibt's nicht mehr und auch keine Fulcrum-Flieger.
Heute flieg' ich meine Runde, seh' Serbien in Trümmern liegen,
Hab'ne HARM am Rail gefunden,
squeeze sie weg und laß' sie fliegen.

A Battle Far Away

Tune: There is a Green Hill Far away

There was a battle far away,
The Puma boys were there,
But where were you, you Bona mates?
We neither know nor care.
2,3,4, 'Cos where were you, you Bona mates?
Where were you, you Bona mates?

Alpha Alert Song

Tune: My Favorite Things

Reading our porno and picking our asses
Checking our forms and passing our gasses
Silver sleek B-61's slung below
Nuclear War and we're ready to go

Chorus:

OOM-PAH PAH, OOM-PAH PAH,
OOM-PAH PAH

Lord Vader watching with all his storm troopers
Cut off your nuts if you answer with bloopers
Certing for him is like shaving with mace
If you screw up he'll rip off your face

Chorus:

Scramble at midnight the engines are turning
Take off in shear fright, our stomachs are churning
Off to the orbit with eye patches on
Shields are all up and the curtains are drawn

Chorus:

Leaving our orbits our pits start to sweat
We'll asshole those fuckers and that's a sure bet
Burn all those Russkies and cover 'em with dirt
That's why we love sitting Alpha Alert

Chorus:

Fulcrums and Flankers and Fishbeds and Floggers
Goas and Gainfuls and BIG GODDAMN BOMBERS
Ganefs and Guidelines and Quad 23's
Thinking of these scares the shit out of me

Chorus:

TF's on hard ride and 200 feet
Crossing the oceans, we've deadlines to meet
Over the mountains we're ready to go
Arming them up and they're all set to blow

Arsehole In Disguise

Tune: Devil in Disguise
(Sung to any obnoxious Jag/Harrier pilot (RAF) etc.)

You look like a pilot, look like a pilot,
You walk like a pilot, walk like a pilot,

Talk like a pilot,
But I got wise,
You're an Arsehole in Disguise,
Oh yes you are
An Arsehole in Disguise
Oh yes you are!

Basra Burns Brightly

Tune: Wir fliegen gegen Engeland

Basra burns brightly on the Tigris,
We bombed the arab bastards day and night, Insch Allah!
For tonight is the Mother of all Battles,
´gainst Saddam´s military might.
Your ships we´hv sank Saddam,
Your Air Force is wank Saddam,
For tonight is the Mother of all battles,
Saddam, Saddam, he´s insane, he´s insane, Insch Allah!

And if I die in battle,
And crash in a fireball in the sand, Boom, Boom,
There is one thing for certain,
The harrier mates didn´t lend a hand.
So where were you, you Harrier Mates?
You couldn´t miss the airshow dates!
So we left you festering at Gutersloh,
Propping, propping up the bar, up the bar, up the bar,
UP YOURS!

B-1 Shake The Ground

Tune: Reggae Beat

People of the land, they say that we are crazy,
Flying low and fast, in the mountains when it's hazy,
My reply to them, yes I'll repeat it once again,
When I'm flying low, I smile allot, no matter where or when!!

Chorus:

B-1 shake the ground,
It make big, big sound,
Everyone screaming and running around,
All fall down!
(Repeat)

Ever since time began, God's been known to shake the land
He shake it high, he shake it low, he make the B-1 that we all know,
And to those who complain the most; they do not laugh, they do not boast;
They live on the land with no fun; while we SHAKE it in the sun!

Chorus:

There are some who like to say, they'd fly a fighter any day;
They've got "Gs", we don't have those, we defy gravity with the MANLY closed:
To those people I'm proud to say, I'd fly the B-1 any day;
The fighter goes round and round, ----
BUT THE B-1 SHAKES THE GROUND!!!

Chorus:

Bloody Great Wheel

Tune: The Froggy Went a Courtin'

An airman told me before he died,
Oh rum-titty, rum-titty, rum-titty, rum.
An airman told me before he died
And I don't think that bastard lied.
Oh rum-titty, rum-titty, rum-titty, rum.
Rum-titty, rum-titty, rum-titty, rum.

He had a wife with a cunt so wide...
That she could not be satisfied.

So he built a bloody great wheel...
With two brass balls and a prick of steel.

The two brass balls were filled with cream...
The whole damn thing was run by steam.

He laid his wife upon their bed...
And tied her legs behind her head.

'Round and 'Round went the bloody great wheel...
And in and out went the prick of steel.

Higher and higher went the level of steam…
Lower and lower went the level of cream.

It fucked his wife until she cried…
"Enough, enough I'm satisfied"

And now we come to the tragic bit…
There was no way of stopping it.

It ripped his wife from ass to tit…
The whole damn room was filled with shit.

Now we come to the part that's grim…
It jumped off her and onto him.
Nine months later a child was bred…
With two brass ball and a bloody great head!

Bone Song

We fly our fucking Bones at 200 fucking feet
We fly our fucking Bones through the rain and snow and sleet
And though we think we're flying south we're flying fucking north
And we haven't seen our wingman since the Firth of fucking Forth

Chorus:

Glory Glory, what a helluva way to die.
Glory Glory, what a helluva way to die.
Glory Glory, what a helluva way to die.
(INSERT LAST LINE OF EACH VERSE)

We fly our fucking Bones at 100 fucking feet
We fly our fucking Bones through the corn and rye and wheat
Though we think we fly with skill, we fly with fucking luck
But we don't give a damn or care a flying fuck

Chorus:

We fly our fucking Bones at 50 fucking feet
We fly our fucking Bones and it's really fucking neat
Though we think we're flying up, we're really flying down
And we bust our fucking asses when we hit the fucking ground

Chorus:
We hate the fucking RCO at the Smokey fucking range

We hate the fucking RCO at the Smokey fucking range
'Cause when we hit the target he says it's off the fucking range
So we roll in on the range tower and that is fucking that

Chorus:

We love the fucking RCO at the Melrose fucking range
We love the fucking RCO at the Melrose fucking range
'Cause when we're 50 miles out he says "You're cleared on hot"
And we get a good score whether we hit the target or not

Chorus:

We fly our fucking Bones at the speed of fucking heat
We fly our fucking Bones and it's quite a fucking treat
With our burners fucking cookin' and our stick pulled fucking back
And there ain't a Bloke among ya who can catch our fucking act

Bosnien-Lied

Hoch über Bosniens Höhen die Sonne glüht,
Unsere Triewerksturbinen singen ihr Lied:
Deutsche TORNADS in Bosnien,
fliegen für Frieden in Jugoslawien.
Es grault die SIDWINDER, es fliegt uns're HARM.
TORNADOS greifen in Bosnien an,
TORNADOS greifen in Bosnien an.

CBUs, Mark 82s

Tune: Bell Bottom Trousers

Once there was a barmaid down in Brewery Lane
Her master was so kind to her, her mistress was the same
Along came a bone driver, handsome as he could be
He was the cause of all her misery!
Chorus: Singing CBUs, Mark 82s
And uniforms of blue
He'll fly a bomber
Like his daddy used to do!

Now in the morning before the break of day
A five-pound note he handed her, and this to her did say:
"Take this my darling, for all the harm I've done

For you may have a daughter, and you may have a son

If you have a daughter, put ribbons in her hair
And if you have a son, get the bastard in the air!"
Now the moral of my story as you can plainly see
Is never trust a aviator an inch above your knee
The barmaid trusted one and he went off to fly
Leaving her a daughter to help the time go by!

FINAL Chorus: Singing CBUs, Mark 82s
And uniforms of blue
She'll never fly a bomber

Cover Of The Weapons Review

Tune: Cover of the Rolling Stone

Well, we're Eagle jocks, we got ten inch cocks,
And we're loved everywhere we go.
We fly for beauty and we fly for truth,
And we make them ragheads glow.
We got all kinds of thrills, we make ya'll kinda ill,
But the thrill we'll never know…

Is the thrill that'll hit 'chya, when ya get your pitcha
On the cover of the WEAPONS REVIEW.
Weapons Review…gonna see my pitcha on the cover.
Review…gonna buy five copies for my mother.
Review…gonna see my smiling face
On the cover of the WEAPONS REVIEW.

Well, we fly Eagle jets and if they give us a war,
We'll kill everything we see.
I got my support package busting their ass for me.
We got all the things that money can buy, but the one thing they'll never do.
Is to put my mug on the front page cover,
Of the latest FIGHTER WEAPONS REVIEW.
Weapons Review…gonna bomb Mosul and Bagdad.

Dashing Through The Sky

Dashing through the sky,
In a Foxtrot one-oh-five,
Through the flak we fly,

Trying to stay alive.

The SAMs destroy your calm,
The MiGs come up to play,
What fun it is to strafe and bomb,
The P.R.V. today!

Chorus: CBUs, Mark 82s, Seven-fifties, too,
Daddy Vulcan strikes again,
Our Christmas gift to you.

Head's up Ho Chi Minh,
The Fives are on their way,
Your luck it has give in,
There's going to be hell to pay.

Today it is our turn,
To make you gawk and stare,
What fun it is to watch things burn,
And blow up everywhere!

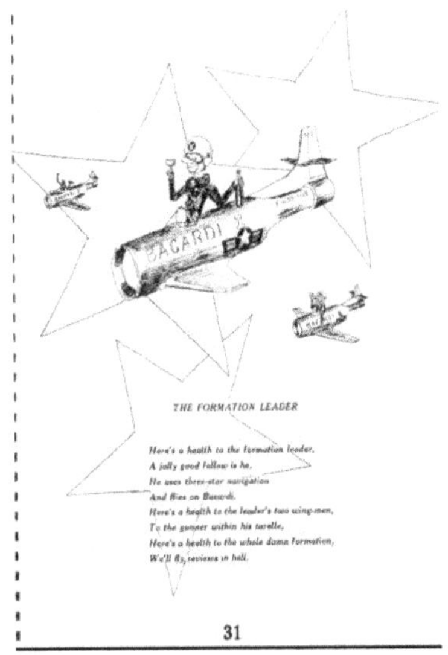
BACARDI

THE FORMATION LEADER

Here's a health to the formation leader,
A jolly good fellow is he,
He uses three-star navigation
And flies on Bacardi.
Here's a health to the leader's two wing-men,
To the gunner within his turelle,
Here's a health to the whole damn formation,
We'll fly [illegible] in hell.

31

Copy from „Three Hats" Songbook

Die grauen TORNADOS

Die grauen TORNADOS ziehen hoch über Land und Meer,
und wo sie erscheinen da fliehen die Feinde vor ihnen her.
Wir lassen uns nicht kriegen,
und schießen die HARM ins Ziel.
Wir schützen die anderen Flieger,
das wird jedem Gegner zu viel.

Wir sind die grauen Husaren der Luft,
die MONSTER, die MONSTER, die MONSTER !
Immer bereit wenn der Einsatz uns ruft,
die MONSTER, de MONSTER, die MONSTER !

Wir stürzen vom Himmel und schlagen zu, wir fürchten die Hölle nicht und geben's zu,
Wir kämpfen bis dass der Feind besiegt. Bis Frieden, bis Frieden, bis Frieden wieder siegt.
Die MONSTER, die MONSTER, die MONSTER !

DO THE RSU SHUFFLE

Tune: is kind of a cross between The Doors "Love Her Madly" & "Riders On The Storm". Sung like a dirge

Do the RSU shuffle
Never use your muscles
Always take it slow
That's how you make your dough
Playing Casino
That's the RSU shuffle (Boogie, Let's Boogie)
Do the RSU shuffle
Never ever hustle
Always say "Yes Sir"
Then you disappear
There's places to hide, On the Maintenance side
That's the RSU shuffle (Boogie, Let's Boogie)
Do the RSU shuffle
Nothing like the "Trenton Bustle"
No one will tell
And Sgt Bull won't yell
If you sleep in the parachute well
That's the RSU shuffle (Boogie, Let's Boogie)
Do the RSU shuffle
There's never a scuffle
Always try & do less
And they'll never guess
You did a 2 hour lunch at the mess
That's the RSU shuffle (Boogie, Let's Boogie)

Don't Bend Down

Tune: My old man

Don't bend down when a Jag mates around,
or he'll stick his Willy up your bum,
he'll keep going, he won't start slowing,
till his knob end is red and glowing
he'll tease you, he'll squezze you,
Do anything to pease you,
try and find an orifice that fits.
But F3s are fighters
we're queer blighters,
and the Jag Mates are bum Bandits.

Jaguares you know, they fly so low,
some even fly into the ground,

they drop bombs
and take nice piccies,
squezze some bottoms,
and suck some dickies,
they'll tease you……etc.

Flying Monsters Song

We are Dirty Bastards,
Scum Of The Earth,
Filth Of Creation,
Mother-Fuckin' Son Of A Bitchin' Fornicator.

Known In Every Whorehouse,
Smoke, Drink and Screw.

We are the FLYING MONSTERS,
Who the fuck are You???

FOX ONE In The Face

Tune: Strangers in the Night.

FOX ONE in the face, you never saw it,
FOX ONE in the face, you really bought it,
at the merge today, we blew your shit away.

Then we came back 'round, you had no SA,
GCI was down, we came back to play,
LIMAS and Gunshots, we finnished off the rest.

Fighting Cocks at night, our hair's on fire,
Fighting Cocks at night, heroes for hire,
But when the sun goes down,
we'll all be downtown
drinking with your wives and girlfriends
while you mend your little egos.
Next time that we meet,
there'll ne no questions,
who you'll have to beat, in any action,
no one fucks or fights.

Went to early briefing, climbed into the kite,
opened the throttles and roared into the night,

leaving the runnway far behind,
it's dark outside, but we don't mind,
'cause we're pressing on regardless,
for the Wing Commanders DFC & BAR.

Fuck Off Treble One

When you're a pilot on a treble one, you're on QRA,
dropping all your Missiles in the firth of tay,
You don't need them, trow them away,
you sit on your barstool drinking milk,
when your work is done, nobody heeds you,
nobody needs you – Fuck Off Treble One!

Hail To The Monsters

Hail t the Monsters, hail 3-2-2 !
Monsters on a mission, men who fight for You.

Flaying ECR by nigh and day,
Killing SAMs which are in our way,
Fight on, fight on – victory's for you,
Boys from 3-2-2.

Happy Landings 90th Squadron

Tune: Cornell Alma Mater

Flying low O're Verdun's trenches, midst the shot and shell.
A pair of dice our lucky emblem, give the huns more hell.
Tail's up and flying any weather, where're the call may be.
Happy landings 90th squadron, hail al hail to thee.

Far above the noise of battle, dodging Archie's fire.
Taking photos far in Hunland, that's our hears desire
(Shout – LIKE HELL)
Tail's up and flying any weather, where're the call may be.
Happy landings 90th squadron, hail al hail to thee.

90th ties can ne'er be broken, wherever we may fly.
Friendships formed in the face of danger, they can never die.
Tail's up and flying any weather, where're the call may be.

Happy landings 90th squadron, hail al hail to thee.

Where're the coming day may find us, what'er the fates prevail.
Memories of our comrades bind us, and we'll never fail.
Tail's up and flying any weather, where're the call may be.
Happy landings 90th squadron, hail al hail to thee.

Hawker-Siddeley Why?

Tune: Why was he born so beautiful

Why were they brought to Gutersloh,
Why were they built at all?
They're no fucking use in peace and war,
They're no fucking use at all!

I Am Viper

Tune: I am Woman

I am Viper, hear me roar,
I am too small to ignore.
Paint me little, paint me tiny, paint me small.
I can sort and pick and choose,
But somehow I always lose.
I guess it's cause I've got no clue at all.
But they said in UPT that the Viper was for me;
That my hands were made of gold and couldn't fail.
My radar just went tits,
Oh My God, ain't this the shits.
I've got Mudhens and Eagles on my tail.

Chorus:

Yes, I am wise but it's feeling from the pain.
Yes, I've paid the price but look at what I've gained.
If I had to, I can do anything,
I am small, I am invincible, I am Viper,
Watch me die!

As I fly the speed of light,
Blowing both ways through the fight,
I know that auto-guns won't let me down.
But I've got no tally-ho,
And I don't know which way to go,
So I guess it's time to slow this mother down.

Hi-aspect at the pass,
First engagement and I'm outta gas,
When the throttle is placed up against the wall.
So I lie here on my back,
With my engine rolling back,
When my GCI controller says – ATOLL!

Chorus:

I Don't Want No More Of Air Force Life

Tune: Gee Ma I wanna Go Home

They say the Mile High Club is really on the rack
that's why everybody, wants to bring the Otters back

Chorus:

> *Oh I don't want no more of Air Force life*
> *Gee Ma I wanna go, back to Ontario*
> *Gee Ma, I wanna go home.*

We polished up the choppers until they really shone
and then we turned them over and cut our fuckin' lawn

They say that in the tool crib the tools are all the best
but every time I need one, the fucking thing's U/S
The women in the squadron are all the decent sort
but they can't wear fur collars 'cause of Master Corporal Shortt

They say that Naccarato has jam between his toes
but he just bends right over and sucks it up his nose

They say that Michael Robinson he climbed up from the bog
now he sleeps in a kennel cause he's a fucking dog

They say that Cam Almasy He really is the boss
we got the word from Dorothy he cums Tobasco sauce

They say that Captain Polo his face went really pale
he looked behind his chopper and he had no fucking tail

They say for Frederick Kuzyk the women they all beg
because he keeps his pecker lock wired to his leg

Now we've know Kevin Lockey since he was a pup

you get him in a classroom and the fucker won't shut up

We know that Kenneth Moores use to live on a farm
the pigs were always pregnant cause Ken slept in the barn

They say that Bob Procyshen is a man of renown
well we think he should prove it and buy a fuckin' round

The women in the squadron they say are really slick
every time you want one they're on someone else's dick

The women in the Reg Force they say are really great
but with all their diseases I'd rather masturbate.

I'd Rather Be An F-4 Jock

(By Dick Jonas)

Well, I'd rather be an F-4 jock,
Than the governor of New York State.
Now, the Governor's got him a pretty good job,
And I suppose he thinks it's great.
But droppin' nape and strafin' trucks,
Are two things he don't know.
And I couldn't fill the Governor's shoes,
"Cause I couldn't spend all that dough.
I started my takeoff, I thought the flaps were down,
But when I pulled the gear up, the speedbrake scraped the ground.
The General smiled at me, he thought it was great fun,
But then I met the FEB, Chitose here I come.

We flew our Sabres through the war, we flew them far and fast,
But when the war was over, we knew it wouldn't last.
They sent our old instructors, to teach us all their tricks,
Now we're flying training, behind those dirty pricks.

Letting down from forty-four, busting through the mach,
That Sabre Jet was moving now, falling like a rock.
My boom was aimed right at the field, there was an awful sound,
Since we're flying training now, I'm sitting on the ground.

I started up into a loop, I thought that I was clear,
I pulled up under Colonel ________, and I thought the end was near.
I went before the FEB, and they gave me the works,

Glory, Glory, Hallelujah, what a bunch of jerks.

Strafin' on the panel, I made my pass to low,
There came a call from Melrose, "One more and home you'll go".
I pulled that Sabre into the blue, she hit a high speed stall,
Now I won't see my mother when the works done this fall.

Now I'm in the gutter, with pretzels in my beer,
With pretzels in my whiskey, I knew the end was near.
Then came this glorious Air Force, to save me from the worst.
Everybody bust a butt and sing the second verse.

I'd rather be an F-4 jock,
Than the owner of old Fort Knox.
And I like the smell of JP-4,
Better than a Rosewood box.
Hydraulic fluid and afterburner fumes,
Just kind of turn me on.
Fella, I'm happier flying F-4Ds,
Than a hound dog gnawing a bone.

Well, I'd rather be an F-4 jock,
Than the Air Force Chief of Staff.
One good reason I ain't got the rank,
Right here you're supposed to laugh.
It's a lot more fun just droppin' bombs,
And hassling two on two.
So, I'll just stick to my gunnery range,
And flying the Phantom II.

Well, one of these days I'll light my fire,
And aim it straight at the sky.
And you'll hear me shout as I disappear,
That a Phantom is the way to fly.
I'll do a high speed pass by the Pearly Gates,
About one point six-five mach.
And I'll tell St. Peter, if he don't mind,
Just make me an F-4 jock.

I'd Rather Fly A Warthog

Oh, I'd rather fly a Warthog,
on a twenty five foot strafing run,
We'll get down in the grass, and kick Ivans ass,

With our 30 mike mike gatling gun.

Oh, don't make me an F-15 jock,
Those bastards sure know how to talk,
You can't press the attack when your engines roll back,
So don't make me an F-15 jock.

Don't give me an Foxtrot One Six,
With a handle instead of a stick,
She'll get on your tail, but the engine will fail,
Don't give me a Foxtrot One Six.

Don't give me an A-7D,
My computers, my manhood to me,
Without his black box, he ain't much of a jock,
So don't give me an A-7D.

Don't give me a Foxtrot Four D,
With two people where one should be,
They train you like Luke, and then give you a nuke,
Don't give me a Foxtrot Four D.

Oh, don't give me a Tango Three Eight,
It's small and it's sleek and it's great.
The'll put you in the pit with hand on your dick,
Oh, don't give me a Tango Three Eight.
Oh, don't fly my hog into a cloud,
Or you'll hear me crying out loud,
They don't pay me the wages to fly on the gauges,
Don't fly my hog in a cloud.

Don't give me a F-104
That airplane's a ground loving whore,
She'll cough and she'll wheeze, and head straight for the trees,
So don't give me a F-104.

Don't give me a Foxtrot 5-E,
An aggressor I don't want to be,
It's tough to get laid, when you're a big training aid,
Oh, don't give me a Foxtrot 5-E.

Don't give me a Phantom Two,
It's TACs two seat B-52,
Drop your bombs, go around, hope they all hit the ground,
Don't give me a Phantom Two.

If I Was A "Jag" Mate

If I was a Jag mate
dida dida dida etc.
All day long I'd stick it up your bum,
If I was a Jaguar man,

I wouldn't have to work hard,
dida dida dida etc.
All day long I'd stick it up your bum,
If I was a Jaguar man.

I'd build them all upstairs
In the middle of the town
Fill it full of Jag mates
With their trousers down
And some of them with nothing at all

I'd take them all upstairs
And stand them in a line
Some of them erect
All are looking fine
And then I'd take them all
One at the time.
Ohhhhhhhhh, if I was a Jag mate....etc.

It's a Long Way to Kuwait City

Tune: Bleeding Obvious

It´s a long way to Kuwait City,
It's a long way to go,
It´s a long way to Kuwait City,
But the Bona mates won´t know,
Goodbye KKMC, farewell Ras-Al-Gar,
It´s a long long way to Kuwait City,
For the Harriers too far.

Sound of the marching feet. (Tramp, tramp, tramp)

Sound of the Daisy Cutters. (Boom, Bbooomm)

Sound of the Burning Iraquis. (EEEEKK)

Sound of the Lost Syrians. (We Surrender Mr Smythe)

It's Hard To Be Humble

Oh Lord, it's hard to be humble,
When you're flying the great B-1B.
I can't wait to strap on my Lancer,
She's one helluva mean gray machine.
To know her is to love her,
By God you know what I mean!
Oh Lord, it's hard to be humble,
When you're flying the great B-1B.

We're proud to be the great Tigers,
We're the best and we just can't be beat.
Just ask Saddam and the Taliban,
They'll tell you we don't know defeat.
To know us is to love us,
To know every ounce of our worth.
Oh Lord, it's hard to be humble,
When you know that you're bombin the earth.

Jolly Tigers

Tune: The Church Has One Foundation

We are the Jolly Tigers,
We went out to Saudi,
There were not many woman,
And even fewer trees,
We would have had a good time if we´d been better led,
But it is our dearest wish that would all drop dead.

Joy To The World

Tune: Joy to the world

Joy to the world, the bombs will come,
let's all go join the fun,
the bridges, dams, and power plants,
the schools, the kids and even ants,
will know the awesome sound,
of bombs hitting the ground.
They'll shiver, The'll quiver,
Gee, war is fun.

KKMC

Tune: Mull Of Kintyre

Oh KKMC, Oh why is it me,
Approaching the Tee
Ehen its too dark to see,
On my NVG.

Up in the morning,
And down to the can,
Sharing the crapper with a strange looking man,
He says I´ll wipe yours arse, if you will wipe mine,
And that keeps us busy til quarter past nine.

Just after the breakfast,
Its down to the brief
There stands a short man, with Reggie beneath,
The usual bullshit, how have they the gall,
As they speak for an our and tellus fuck-all.

Three hours later
To the Int brief we go,
It´s given once daily by a man called the GLO,
He says he can´t help us-we think it's a farce,
I can get loads more Int from the cheeks of my arse.

Long Range Active AMRAMM

Tune: Peaceful Easy Feeling

I like the way the missile contrail streaks
Across the sky so blue
I shot that thing a few miles ago
It's already lookin' for you

Chorus:

> *Cause I shot a long range active AMRAMM*
> *And I know it won't let me down*
> *Cause I've already turned my jet around*

And I found out a long time ago
What a slammer can do to your soul
When it finds the MiG it's lookin' for
Next thing you know it's a smokin' hole

Chorus:

I get this feeling I should leave now
And leave it up to my little friend
My spikes no longer screamin' in both of my ears
That tells me I will never see you again

Chorus:

OOHH, OOHH
Smokin' Hole

Mary Jo Kapeckne

Oh your ass is like a stovepipe, Mary Jo Kapeckne.
And the nipples on your tits are turning green.
There's a thousand crabs abounding from your pussy.
You're the ugliest fuckin' bitch I've ever seen.

There's a pound of lint protruding from your navel.
When you piss, you piss a stream of grass.
There's enough wax in your ear to make a candle.
So please make one now and shove it up you ass.

If you'd live to be a gray-haired wonder,
Keep your nose out of the blue.
Flying men, guarding the nation's border,
We'll be their, followed by more.
In echelon, we carry on,
Nothing'll stop the U.S. Air Force!

My Husband

My husband's a Colonel, a Colonel, a Colonel,
A very fine Colonel is he,
All day he makes plans, he makes plans, he makes plans,
and at night he comes home and makes me.

Chorus:

Oh, sing a little bit, fuck a little bit, follow the band, follow the band, follow the band,
Oh, sing a little bit, fuck a little bit, follow the band, follow the band, join in our happy song.

My husband's a Major, a Major, a Major,
A very fine Major is he,
ll day he chews ass, chews ass, chews ass,
and at night he comes home and chews me.

Chorus:

My husband's a Captain, a Captain, a Captain,
A very fine Captain is he,
All day he fucks up, fucks up, fucks up,
At night he comes home and fucks me.

Chorus:

My husband's a Lieutenant, a Lieutenant, a Lieutenant,
a very fine Lieutenant is he,
All dayhe eats shit, eats shit, eats shit,
and at night he comes home and eats me.

Chorus:

My husband's a WSO, a WSO, a WSO,
A very fine WSO is he,
All day he rides Eagles, rides Eagles, rides Eagles,
and at night he comes home and rides me.

My Way

Tune: My Way

And now, the end is near, and so I face the final curtain,
I lost my outboard tanks, my guns, my bombs, my wings,
I'm certain.
I planned the mission well, I briefed to fly right down the
highway, I armed it up and pickled once, and did it my way.

Regrets, I have a few, they disapproved my last extension,
They've cast a jaundiced eye upon the need for my retention.
I flew the day before, I logged my time, not is a shy way,
I guess I should have logged much more, but I did it my way.

Well, there were times, I'm sure you knew,

When you were good, but I was too,
The scores come back, you had your doubt,
I'd won it all, I'd cleaned you out,
Today that's changed I missed the range, But hit the highway.

I've loved, I've laughed and cried, I've had my fill, my share of losing,
And now they way I lied, but I don't care, it's so amusing.
My boss discussed the flight, each detailed step, along the byway,
And then he said, "Don't use your head, just do it my way"

But I've got to stand on my two feet,
So keep your kids off of the street.
I've got to fly, and fight, and sing,
To keep my cool and do my thing.
I'll cross the seas, And even kill the trees
But I'll do it MY WAY

Nape

Tune: Tea for Two

Nape is great, so hit my grids.
It burns, it bakes, it sticks to kids.
Nape is great, so drop it on their heads.
And make their eyes pop out!

When you drop a can or two.
It burns, it bakes, it sticks like glue.
Nape is great, so drop it on their heads.
And make their eyes pop out!

Napalm Sticks To Kids

We shoot the sick, the young, the lame,
We do our best to maim.
Because all the kills count the same,
Napalm sticks to kids.

Chorus:

NAPALM STICKS TO KIDS
NAPALM STICKS TO KIDS

Flying low across the trees,
Pilots doing what they please,
Dropping frags on refugees,
Napalm sticks to kids.

Gooks in the open, making hay,
But I can hear the gunships say,
"There'll be no Chieu Hoi today",
Napalm sticks to kids.

I've only seen it happen twice,
Both times it was mighty nice,
Shooting peasants planting rice,
Napalm sticks to kids.

See those farmers over there,
Watch me get them with a pair,
Blood and guts everywhere,
Napalm sticks to kids.

On The Wing Again

On the wing again
Just can't wait to get on the wing again,
The life I love I flying Eagles with my friends,
So I can't wait to get on the wing again.

On the wing again,
Going places that I've never been,
Bombing things I may never bomb again,
I can't wait to get to the wing again.

On the wing again,
Like a tribe of Injuns we roar down from the skyway
We're the best of friends,
Insisting that te bombs keep falling our way
Spiking our way.

I'll be "two"again,
Just can't to be old "Chief Two" again,
The life I love is flying Eagles with my friends,
Oh. I can't wait to be old "Chief Two"again.

On Top Of The Pop Up

On top of the pop up, and flat on my back
I lost my poor wingman, in a big hail of flak
Guard channel was silent, the sites were all dead

Until we rolled in, and looked up ahead.

The sky filled with fire, the missiles flashed by
Sweet mother of Jesus, we're all going to die.
Number two called "I'm hit, I'm going to bust!"
Not one goddamned Elint a poor jock can trust.

So come ye young pilots, and listen to dad
Forget about jinking, and your ass has been had.
They'll hit you, they'll burn you, their flak reaches far
It's a long walk to Takhli, and a beer in the bar.

Over Serbian Skies

Now listen all you airman, young and old,
To the tales of fighter pilots, young and bold,
With their fighters loaded and big,
Taking off to contact "MAGIC",
In the crisp Serbian air so blue and cold.

It was, save the KOSOVO from all the Serbs,
2 HARMS loaded, this time hot and not inerts,
4 Jets lined up on the runway,
Wish I'd gone to church on Sunday,
Hoping we bring back home all of our birds....
Singing hi-hi-yipee-yipee-yeh,.........

Twenty thousend over NIS and heading west,
ECR is shooting HARM, he's NATO's best.
GOA and GAINFUL are suckers,
We will kill those motherfuckers,
And ot "Schützenfest" we give "SLOBO" the rest.

PIA Tower, this is CANNON, flight of four,
We are heading home, we're through with this damn war.
We are flying inbound HOMEPLATE,
to the palce, where our girls wait,
'cause there's finally nothing left to fight on for.

Singing hi-hi-yipee-yipee-yeh,.........

Que Sera

When I was just a little boy, I asked my father what will I be?
Will I be a Pilot? Will I be a Nav?
Here's what he said to me:
Que sera, sera, Three-Two-Two will always be,
The Champion of Germany, Three-Two-Two 322.

Sengo's Song

Sengo was a lazy coon,
went to sleep in the afternoon,
so tired was he,
so very, very tired was he.

Off to the jungle he did go,
swinging his chopper to and fro,
when along came a bee,
a fucking great bumble bee.
(bzzz, bzzz, bzzz, bzzz)

Fly away you bumble bee,
I ain't no rose,
I ain't no syphlic prick,
get off my fucking nose.

Get off my nasal organ,
don't you come near,
if you want some fanny,
you can fuck my granny,
but you'll get no arseholes here,
No fear,
Just beer.

Arseholes rule the NAVY,
Arseholes rule the NAVY,
Arseholes rule the NAVY,
You'll get no arseholes here,
No fear,
Just beer.

Stark wie noch nie

Fliegen das ist unser Leben, SAM – ites gibt es viel zu viel,
Darum schießen wir die Monster uns're HARM auf jedes Ziel,
Die Crews in uns'ree Staffel sind die besten Crews der Welt,
Sie sind treu wie gute Freunde für die nur das Fliegen zählt.

Wir sind stark wie noch nie, stark wie noch nie!
Wir haben MONSTER – POWER uns zwingt keiner in die Knie.
Wir sind stark wie noch nie, stark wie noch nie!
Die FLYING MONSTERS die sind jetzt stark wie noch nie!

Starfighter-Song (F-104 G)

by Ekki Südmeyer

This is a Strafighter song, before you see it, it'll be gone,
it's the prettiest bird up in the sky.
Starfighter, moonlight and lovesongs,
that's where us 104 jocks belong.

You've gotta be cool, You've got to be mean,
You'll be a fighter pilot down in the seam,
You've gotta fly her using your touch,
and then this old girl's gonna like you very much.

Starfighter song, before you see it, it'll be long, long gone……

She's the prettiest plane that You've ever seen,
although, when she's loaded, she looks godamn mean,
and when you ride her high she goes way up in the sky,
some people say, they don't know why.
They say, she's old, I say she is timeless,
They say she's old, well I say it's the fastest bird around.

That's why I sing a Starfighter song……..

Yes my 104, she oks like a toy,
and to see her fly, fills anyone with joy,
but you hear all sorts of comments lke: "man – what a deal"
I tell you: Watch out, babe, when she plays for real !
They say she's old, I say she's timeless,
They say she's slow, well I say it's the fastest bird around.
Starfighter song, before you see it, it'll be……..

Serbien-Lied

Ja in Serbien gab es früher viele SAM-Sites,
so wie die GAINFUL, die GOA und GUIDLINE.

Ja ob STRAIGHT FLUSH, FLAT FACE,
LONG TRACK oder BAR LOCK,
Uns're Missile hat auf jedes Radar Bock.

In Serbien schießen wir die Radars aus,
wir bringen keine HARM heut' mit nach Haus.

Wir schießen HARM bei Tag und Nacht,
ECR-TORNADO !
Wir sind die NATO – SEAD – Macht.
ECR-TORNADO !

Ob Pilot oder WSO,
ECR-TORNADO !
Ein MAGNUM macht uns alle froh,
Oh MAGNUM – HORRIDO !

Sitting On QRA

Tune: Dock of the Bay

Sitting on QRA, watching the time waste away,
sitting on QRA, wasting time.
I left my home in Leuchars,
headed for the firth of tay,
we've had no BEARS or BADGERS,
seems like no things gonna come our way.

We're jus sitting QRA.......

Looks like nothings gonna change,
everything remains the same,
I can do what ten men can do,
but I just sit here sining my refrain.

Just sitting on QRA.....

Son's Comin' Home

Son's Comin' home in a body bag, do da do da,
Son's comin' home in a body bag oh dadoo da day.

Chorus:
Mother Fucker's dead, never found his head,
Son's comin' home in a body bag oh dadoo da day.

Got shot down by an SA-2, do da do da,
Got shot down by an SA-2, oh dadoo da day.

Tried to punch out way too late, do da do da,
Tried to punch out way too late, oh dadoo da day.

Now he's just a blob of Goo, da do da do,
Now he's just a blob of Goo, oh dadoo, da day.

South Atlantic Hornpipe

Tune: Drunken Sailor.

What shall we do with the Argentinians?
What shall we do with the Argentinians?
What shall we do with the Argentinians?
Early in the morning?

Nuke, nuke, nuke the bastards,
Nuke, nuke, nuke the bastards,
Nuke, nuke, nuke the bastards,
Early in the morning.

What shall we do with a Mirage 3?
Smash him in the face with a skyflash missile

What shall we do with an A-4 Skyhawk?
Stuff him up the arse with an AIM-9 LIMA

What shall we do with a PUCA-ARA?
Gun him on the ground before he's airborne

What shallwe do with the "Argie Ground Troops"?
Strafe, strafe, strafe the bastards

What shall we do with the "Argies Widows"?

Shoot her sons and fuck her daughters.

Strafe The Town And Kill The People

Tune – Wake the Town and Tell the People

Strafe the town and kill the people
Drop your napalm in the square
Roll in early Sunday morning
Try to catch them all at prayer.

Spread your CBU down mainstreet
See the arms and legs and hair
Watch them crawling for the clinic
Put a pod of rockets there.

Sprinkle candy in the courtyard
Watch the orphans gather 'round
Use your 20 millimeter
Mow those little bastards down.

Find a field of running Charlies
Drop a Daisy-Cutter there
Watch the chunks of bodies flying
Arms and legs and blood and hair.

See the fat, old pregnant woman
Running 'cross the field in fear
Run you 20 mike-mike through her
Hope your film comes out real clear.
Spray the crops and kill the farmers
Spray them with your poison gas
Watch them throwing up their breakfast
As you make your second pass.

Strafe the town and kill the people
Drop your high drag on the school

Review....gonna spull little HADJI.
Review....gotta see my smiling face,
On the stinkin' FIGHTER WEAPONS REVIEW

In our Eagle jet we'll be somebody,
With thirty thousand pounds of gas.
Gonna punch off my BRU's, get my heater's cookin'

Mach one oh at the pass.
And when my bomb strings tight, the Ragheads filled with fright'
As I blow his ass in two!
But after all this glory, they won't give me no stinkin' story,
In the stinking FIGHTER WEAPONS REVIEW.
Weapons Review....gonna see my pitcha on the cover.
Review...gonna buy five copies for my mother.
Review...gotta see my smiling face,
On the cover of the FIGHTER WEAPONS REVIEW!

Strike Song

Please release me, let me go, I don't love you anymore,
I don't care who's friend or foe,
so please release me, let me nuke them till they glow.

I've been sitting "Q" all day long,
and I'm getting sick and tired of this song.
Too long you told me to keep it cool,
so release me, 'cause I sure in't no fool.....Please...

If you're aware of what I've said,
you know I ain't no toy with which to bet.
You don't play games with nukes and yields.
They'll blow up in your face, your ass and heels.

So please release me, let me go,
if you still want the face of the earth to glo,
to live together ain't no sin,
if you believe that, then pull your nukes back in.

T-38 Song

Take me up, up in the sky, where I'm gonna be flying high,
Take me down and around the clouds where I can play,
I've been high, I've been low and goddamnit, I've been slow,
But she'll be always my best mate, Yeap me T-38.

Oh when I fly her it makes me feel free, as long as I don't over-"G"
Her and then get the feeling I've met,
That the IP hits you over the head,
But when you're solo, you're free as can be,
In the sky, the clouds and debris

Of the twoship you hit over "GIN"
Although that's nowhere to close to whrer you should have been,
Take me up, up in the sky.......

Then there's that feeling, that feeling I keep
About that time I was still flying "Tweet" (like fucking sheep)
Yes, when we flew "Blue I was Blue 2"
And a mere 300 knots was about all you could do.
But it's all over now, That's all I can say,
Though one more thing I'd like to mention if I may.

The 400 Squadron Song (400 Sqn's a hell of a place)

(Author unknown, but obviously brilliant!)

400 squadron's a hell of a place,
The organization's a bloody disgrace,
It's run by a Wing CO who hasn't a clue,
Especially up here at old Downsview.

A weekend trip was promised to us,
If we can't fly you we'll take you by bus,
All that we saw was the bloody canteen,
To hell with those men & their flying machines.
Our CO says we must be looking our best,
Our shoes must be shiny, our uniforms pressed,
The shine on our shoes, you can tell at a glance,
Will never compare with the ass of his pants.
I believe there was more , something like:
"Warrants & sergeants all gentleman true,
hands in there pockets with nothing to do"...
Do you know any other verses? Or the name of the tune it was based on?

Thanks to Doug (& The Slugs) Watkins for providing the missing bits.

The Alpha Man

Tune: The Candy Man

Who can make a sunrise,
Sprinkle it with dust,
Loose a million megatons,
Turn your skin to crust.

Chorus:

The Alpha Man can

The Alpha Man can
The Alpha Man can 'cause he dials up the yield
And makes the world glow

Who can take tomorrow,
Blow it all away,
Send us to the Stone Age,
In just a single day.

Chorus:

The Alpha Man makes,
Everything he bakes,
Crisp and black and unattractive,
Desolate and quite inactive.
And don't forget radioactive,
Who can make a sunrise,
Sprinkle EMP,
Drop a silver bullet,
And don't wait to see.

Chorus:

Dear Saddam Hussein
You are an asshole,
You'd fuck all Islam,
To reach your own goal,
You may think you're shit hot,
But we know the score,
Your father fucks goats,
And your mother's a whore!

Chorus:

The Argentinian Song

Tune: What shall we do with the drunken sailor

What shall we do with the Argentinians? (x3) Earlie in the morning....

Nuke, nuke, nuke the bastards, (x3) Earlie in the morning....

A-4 Skyhawk	Stuff him up the arse with an Aim-9L.
Mirage III	Smash him in the face with a Skyflash missile.
Pucahara	Gun him on the ground before he's airborne.

Argie ground troops	Nape, nape, napalm the bastards.
(with reverance):	
Old Belgrano	Send him to the bottom with a big torpedo
Argie widows	Shoot their sons and fuck their daughters

The Bone Squadron Song

Waltz

Back in '81 a man named Ronnie has some fun,
He said build a bomber and I'll call it the B-1,
Now the Cold War was ragin',
The Buff she was agin',
The King of the Bombers her day was almost done.

In stepped Mr. Rockwell with a blueprint and a grin,
He said give the word and Ronnie TOLD HIM TO BEGIN,
So the (Sq callsign) started flyin',
The Commies started cryin'.
So let's all

DRINK BEER – DRINK BEER – DRINK BEER

OH COME DRINK BEER WITH ME

FOR I DON'T GIVE A DAMN FOR ANY ONLD MAN WHO WON'T DRINK BEER WITH ME!!
(Drinking Tune)

Roll out that old metal keg with FUMU's head upon it
HEAD! WHO SAID HEAD?! I'LL TAKE SOME OF THAT!

Then we'll all have another glass of beer, MORE BEER!
For it's not for glory that we tell our story
But to raise hell while we're, get a little wilder, raise hell while we're here.

(Fight Song)

And we will drink, drink, drink to the (Squadron)
And we will raise our glasses high
And we will drink to our beloved Bomber THE BONE!
There is no better in the sky IN THE SKY!
Oh how we love to come in hard and low
There is no other we'd rather fly

And when the day is done we'll drink JUST ONCE!
To the Bone and the (Squadron)

The Blunts and the Remfs and the Ponties

Tune: My Bonnie Is Over The Ocean

230 we send them to Ireland,
230 we send them to war,
The Blunts and the Remfs and the Pontis
Are posted to 3 and to 4.

They called in the Anglo-French Jaguar,
They called in Tornado and Buc,
They left out the 5's and the 7's,
'Cos we know their not worth a fuck.

Bring back, bring back, bring back the GR3 to me,
Bring back, bring back, the GR3.

The Cope North Rodeo Song

Tune – You Piss Me Off

Oh, it's 40 below, and it don't mean a thing
I got heaters on my wing, and I'm off to the RODEO!

Chorus:

Lead break left, Two's lost sight
Com'on ya fucking dummy, get your right nine right.
Stay on my wing, you God Damn dude, ya know…
You piss me off, you fucking jerk, You get on my nerves!

Oh, I'm ten from the merge, and my radar's a mort
I don't have a sort, and I'm off to the RODEO.

Well, the hell with a heater, Gonna have some fun
I'm closing for guns, and I'm off to the RODEO

Chorus:

Well, here comes a Panther pilot with his pecker in his hand
He's a one balled man, and he's off to the RODEO!

Final Chorus:

Tally three, save a VIPER for me
Com'on, ya little fucker, let me see 9 G's
I call a kill, you don't kill remove ya know…
You piss me off, You fucking jerk, You get on my nerves!

The fighters checked right in, BOLARS two by two.
Low on gas, and the tanker overdue.
They asked the FAC to mark, just where that truck was parked.
MMM, MMM, MMM
The Bronc, he rolled right in, with his smoke to mark,
Exactly where that truck was parked.
But the rest is in doubt, 'cause he never pulled out.
MMM, MMM, MMM

(With Reverence)
Dear mom, your son is dead, he bought the farm today.
He crashed his OV-10 on Ho Chi Mihn's highway.
He made a rocket pass, and then he busted his ass.
HIM, HIM, FUCK HIM!

How did he go/ STRAIGHT IN!!
What was he doing? ONE SIXTY NINE!!
Hell of a deal. WHOOEE!!

Cocksucker, motherfucker, eat a bag of shit.
Cunt hair, douche bag, bite your mother's tit.
We're the BEST COMBAT SQUADRON, all the others suck!!
Tiger, Tiger, Tiger--- RAH RAH FUCK!!

The Flag

Sung by British Pilots, **Germans were quiet and looked away**!

The Flag flies high on the mast head,
we'll drink to the freedom of the Reich.
No longer will we tremble,
at England's military might.
So give to me your hand, Fraulein,
your lilly-white hand, Fraulein,
for tonight we march against England,
England, England's Isle shores,
Island shores, Island shores.

And if I fall in Battle,

and sink to the bottom of the sea,
splish, splash,
remember this my darling,
my blood was shed for Thee,
so give to me your hand, Fraulein,
your lilly-white hand, Fraulein,
for tonight we march against England,
England, England's Isle shores,
Island shores, Island shores.

The Harrier's War Role

Tune: The Church has one Foundation

The Harrier ´s a funny looking aircraft,
It flies across the Mohne dam, Mohne dam.
Does this aircraft have a war role,
Try and find one if You can!

Its picture´s always found in Zeitung,
It tours the airshow all year round, all year round,
But when the Tigers fought the Saudi,
The Harrier was nowhere to be found.

The Marauder

The Marauder's a very fine aircraft
Constructed of rivets and tin
Top speed well over three hundred
Especially when you're in a spin.

chorus:
Oh why did I join the Air Corps?

Mother, dear mother knew best
Here I lie 'neath the wreakage
Marauder all over my chest.

The Music Man

LEADER: I am the music man, and I come from down the way
And I can P-L-A-Y…

Chorus:

What can you P-L-A-Y?

LEADER: I can play the B-1 pilot.

Chorus:

Fuckin' A, My wings won't work, won't work, won't work

VERSES:

A-10 Pilot......................Leavin' today, get there next week
F-14 Pilot.......................My pussy hurts, Tailhook, tailhook
F-15 Pilot.......................I lost sight, lost sight, lost sight
F-16 Pilot.......................I blacked out
Fishbed Pilot...................Outta gas, Outta gas
Flanker Pilot...................My Wanker's on fire
Shithouse door..................Banga, banga, banga, banga
Michael Jackson................My hair's on fire
Sperm whale....................Spew some beer

The North Atlantic Squadron

Tune: Come on, you know it!

There was an old whore from Montreal whose cunt spread from wall to wall
but all she got was sweet fuck all from the North Atlantic Squadron.

Chorus:...
Away, away with fife & drum, here we come, full of rum
looking for women to peddle their bum, in the North Atlantic Squadron

The cabin boy, the cabin boy, the dirty little nipper ,
he tried to screw a .22 & someone pulled the trigger.

The cabin boy, the cabin boy, the dirty little nipper,
he stuffed his ass with fibreglass & circumcised the skipper.

The cabin boy, the cabin boy, the dirty little nipper,
he stuffed his bum with bubblegum & vulcanized the skipper.

The surgeon said the girls were clean, the son of a bitch was off his beam,
the end of my prick is turning green, in the North Atlantic Squadron.

There was a girl from Labrador, she spread her legs from door to door, but all she got was a 2 by 4, from the North Atlantic Squadron .

The eskimo women they are the pits, they have no box, they have no tits, they whack you off with their furry mitts, in the North Atlantic Squadron. The Newfie girls they are no catch, all they do is pick & scratch,
and pull the crabs out of their snatch, in the North Atlantic Squadron.

There was a girl from Moosenee, who spread her legs from tree to tree, all she got was some VD, from the North Atlantic Squadron.

There was a girl from PEI, who came to Toronto very shy,
the 400 men gave her a try, now for 2 bucks she'll service any guy.
In days of old when knights were bold and condoms weren't invented, they wrapped their socks around their cocks & babies were prevented.

In days of old when knights were bold and women weren't particular, they lined them all against the wall & fucked them perpendicular.

The pilot's name was Lester, he was a hymen tester,
Through cherries thick he shoved his prick & left it there to fester.

We've flown the seas & oceans too, and fucked women of every hue, our dongs and balls are black & blue, we're the North Atlantic Squadron.

The Saddam Hussein Song

Tune: Sweet Betsy from Pike

We see the plot thicken
We know what's in store
Your country wants trouble
It's begging for more
You say that you'll bring them
True grace from Islam
But the Air Force will bring on
The first load of bombs

Chorus:

So it's rags, rags, rags on our head
Rags, rags, rags o-o-o-n your head
So it's rags, rags, rags on your head
Tomorrow you'll wake up and find yourself dead!

Dear Iraqi people
We'll bring you some food
Some curry and goat meat
It will be so good
So fix up some kebabs
And hope for the best
We'll bring the napalm
And cook up the rest.

Chorus:

You pompous old faggot
You cant get it up
So drop your beret
And take a big suck
You impotent bastard
You'll be on the run
When we roll in tracking
And lazing for fun

The Scud Missiles

Tune: John Peel

Well a Scud missile blew me out of my bed,
So I rushed to the GLO and to him I said,
I don´t give a toss, report me to my boss,
Cause Saddam´s coming down in the morning.

Do ya ken Al Jubayl where the sun shines bright,
And ya dream all day of a solit shite,
Stay down your foxhole
With your egg and bacon roll
Do ya like bromide tea in the morning.

Do ya ken Bahrain where the Jags mates are,
And the gay boy loiters propping up the bar,
Their new squadron toys,
Are 12 little arab boys,
Stuff your arse with glass in the morning.

Do ya ken Dahran with an in coming Scud
And ya cant hold ya breath, so ya pray that it's a dud
It will spoil your day
As your skin falls away

And ya get a funny twitch in the morning.

Do ya ken the Argos with its turbulent deck.
When ya hit the superstructure you´ll break ya fucking neck
thre´s a nursey down below
Who´s suspenders are on show
And you´ll get a little prick in the morning (O yes you will)

Do ya ken the dessert cabs don't they look quaint,
Three weeks late and peeling pink paint,
The flare gun´s at the door,
´Cos wehaven´t got Mode 4,
With a Stinger up Your arse in the morning.

Those Were The Days

Tune: Mary Hopkins

Once there was a time we had it easy,
when we were forgotten and content;
then there came around a "real" mission,
now our life is no-fly-zones and tents...

Those were the days, my friend
we thought they'd never end
we'd drink our fill, until our livers rot;
and though we'd sometimes fret
about the Russian threat,
we didn't care about the world a lot.

Then one day Saddam Hussein made trouble,
Bosnia got play on CNN;
The UN flocked to us upon the double,
what a change between the now and then--

Those were the days, my friend
we thought they'd never end
we had the time to take a bit of leave;
though now you laugh and smile,
there was a time awhile,
when rules and regs were easy to believe.

One day I awoke to see the sad truth
that we're caught forever in a rut;
though we now may be upright and moral,
still I miss the days we could be sluts.

Those were the days my friend,
through strip bars end-to-end
we'd sing and dance, until our cash was gone;
carousing like a fool
when Tailhook sounded cool,
they say we're wrong, but somehow we got along!

Tracking Kill

Tune: Cover of the Rolling Stone

Well, we're Eagle drivers, we ain't 9 to 5'ers, we're the best that's ever been.
Well, we shoot'em in the face, 'cause that's the very best place to kill and live to fight again.
Yeah, we shoot'em in the face, 'cause that's the real neat place, and it gives us quite a thrill.
But the thrill that'll get ya, is when you set your pipper, and make a guns tracking kill!

Chorus:

TRACING KILL....
Wanna see you in my pipper.
KILL....
Gonna show the film to your sister
KILL....
Gonna make you a great big star in the movies of a tracking kill!

We wear go fast pants, and snappy hard hats, and fly off to shoot down planes
Well we get our kicks ripping off their lips, gunning out the bad guys brains
Yeah, the Aim-9L, it's really swell, but the thing that'll make your day,
Is to place your sights, till it feels just right, and blow a MiG's shit away!
Chorus:

We've paid our dues, got a bag of clues, the job's really lot's of fun.
Well, we never tire of our hair on fire, and killing people with our gun.

Yeah, the Strike Eagle jet is the best you can get, the world's greatest fighting Machine.
To the men that fly her, you can get no higher, than the McDonnells's mighty F-15E.
Chorus:

Two Month Late

Tune: Side by Side

The Pumas went to Saudi in 90,
We thought we´d left the Chinhooks in blighty
When bugger me,
In January,
Who arrived?
Along came a gaggle of, Wokkas,
Flown by Sqn of, plonkers,
They thought that out here,
They´d find woman and beer
Pigs might fly.

The Navy followed on soon, after,
Their quickstops provided much, laughter,
Yes the fishheads went pale,
When they snapped off a tail,
Nice Cat 5!

The Air Corps also had a small, calamity,
They amended Newtons law of, gravity,
What goes up, must come down,
And smash in the ground.
Ondor time!

Well the Wokkas soon had a big, surprise,
Their Boss announced it wasn´t an, exercise.
They said we thought it was strange-
This is a fuckinge range
Who´s on our side?

Along came the mother of all, battles,
SH collected all their, medals
Now it´s back home we go,
To let the Harriers know
SH are the boys.

What Shall We Do With A Hopeless Leader

Tune: What shall we do with a drunken sailor

What shall we do with a hopeless leader,
What shall we do with a hopeless leader,
What shall we do with a hopeless leader, early in the morning.

Send, send, send him to ASOC,
Take him off Ops and put him on Training,
Make him i/c POWs,
AMF arrest more friendlies,
send him, send him to Force Headquaters

What Shall We Do With......

What shall we do with Iraqi Fulcrums,
What shall we do with Iraqi Fulcrums,
What shall we do with Iraqi Fulcrums, earli in the morning?

Shoot 'em in the face with a Sparrow missile,
Shoot 'em in the face with a Sparrow missile,
Shoot 'em in the face with a Sparrow missile, earli in the morning.

What shall we do with Iraqi Floggers......
Shoot 'em up the ass with an AIM 9 Lima.......

What shall we do with Iraqi helos........
Blow 'em straight to hell with an LGB oh.......

What shall we do with Iraqi soldiers.......
Burn away their flesh with incendiaries.........

What shall we do with Iraqi widows......
Shoot their sons and fuck their daughters......

We Fly Our Fucking Fighters

Tune: Battle Hymn of the Republic

We fly our fucking fighters at two hundred fucking feet
We fly our fucking fighters through the rain and snow and sleet
And though we thinking we're flying south we're flying fucking north
And we haven't seen our wingman since the Firth of fucking Forth

Chorus:

Glory, glory what a helluva way to die
Glory, glory what a helluva way to die
Glory, glory what a helluva way to die
(Last line of previous verse)'

We fly our fucking fighters at one hundred fucking feet
We fly our fucking fighters through the corn and rye and wheat
And though we think we fly with skill, we fly with fucking luck
But we don't really give a damn or care a flying fuck

We fly our fucking fighters at just fifty fucking feet
We fly our fucking fighters and it's really fucking neat
And though we think we're flying up, we're really flying down
And we bust our fucking asses when we hit the fucking ground

We fly our fucking fighters at the speed of fucking heat
We fly our fucking fighters and it's really quite a treat
With burners fucking cookin' and the stick pulled fucking back
There ain't a bloke among ya who can catch our fucking act.

Wir fliegen ECR-TORNADO

Hier bei uns im Süden, wo wir Flying Monsters fliegen,
hier sind wir zu Hause, kein Tiger wird uns jemals kriegen.

In uns'ren Kampfmaschinen steig'n wir zur Sonne empor,
wir kämpfen bis wir siegen, uns macht keiner was vor.

Wir fliegen ECR-TORNADO,
fliegen ECR-TORNADO,
Wir fliegen ECR-TORNADO
Und singen Horrido Johoo. (2x)
Shalala-lalalalala 3x)......
We are the FLYING MONSTERS !!!

TLP „Fighter Pilot Songs"

A Lightning Flash Production:

Unofficial Fighter Pilots Songbook

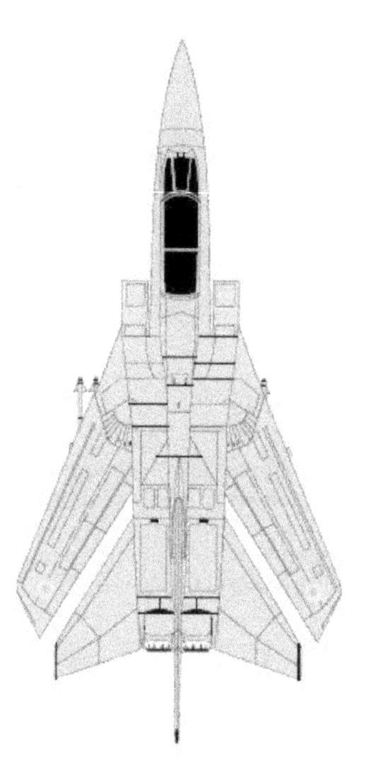

A compilation of songs, poems and quotes from Messes, Officers Clubs and Crewrooms.

THE "LOW LEVEL" SONGS

A Prayer

Tune: Ach, Du lieber Augustin

(Spoken)
Leader: And now, gentlemen, a prayer. A prayer for the constipated!
Pack: SHIT!
Leader: A prayer for the frustrated!
Pack: FUCK!
Leader: A prayer for the dehydrated!
Pack: BEER!
Leader: A prayer for the emasculated!
Pack: BALLS!

Balls to Mr. Benglestein, Benglestein, Benglestein,
Balls to Mr. Benglestein, dirty old man.

He sits on the steeple and shits on the people,
So balls to Mr. Benglestein, dirty old man.

He keeps us all waiting while he's masturbating,
So balls to Mr. Benglestein, dirty old man.

He ups and he downs them, he fucking well grinds them,
So balls to Mr. Benglestein, dirty old man.

A Cold Winter's Evening

'Twas a cold winter's evening, the guests were all leaving
O'Leary was closing the bar
When he turned and he said to the lady in red,
"Get out, you can't stay where you are."
She wept a sad tear in her bucket of beer
As she thought of the cold night ahead,
When a gentleman dapper stepped out of the crapper,
And these are the words that he said:

"Her mother never told her
the things a young girl should know,
about the ways of Air Force men
the way they come and go.
Age has taken away her beauty,

And sin has left its sad scar
So remember your mothers and fuck all the others,
And let her sleep under the bar."

Aahlawetta

Tune: Alouette
(Unsuspecting female volunteer needed)

Chorus:

Aahlawetta, Shoneton Aahlawetta,
Aahlawetta, Shoneton Aahlaw-way.

Leader: Does she have ze stringy hair?
All: Oui, she has ze stringy hair.
Leader: Stringy hair,
All: Stringy hair,
Leader: Aahlawette! Aah, aah, aah . . .

Chorus:

Leader: Does she have ze furrowed brow?
All: Oui, she has ze furrowed brow,
Leader: Furrowed brow,
All: Furrowed brow,
Leader: Stringy hair,
All: Stringy hair,
Leader: Aahlawette! Aah, aah, aah . . .

Wooden eye (Yes I would!) . . .
Broken nose . . .
Two buck teeth . . .
Double chin . . .
Swinging tits . . .
Beer belly . . .
Bulbous butt . . .
Bedroom eyes . . .
Blow job lips . . .
Tell-tale hole . . .
Furry thing . . .
Mack truck cunt . . .

Chorus:
Leader/all: How I love her (repeat all)

Ah Sweet Mystery Of Life

Oh, your asshole's like a stovepipe, Nelly, darling,
And the nipples on your tits are turning green,
There's a million crabs a-bounding on your pussy,
Your the ugliest bitch I've ever seen.

There's a yard of lint protruding from your navel,
When you piss, you piss a stream as green as grass,
There's enough wax in your ears to make a candle,
So why not make one, dear, and shove it up your ass!

Along The Northeast Railroad (Vietnam)

Along the Northeast Railroad, one bright and sunny day
By the wreckage of his Thunderchief the young pursuer lay
His parachute hung from a nearby tree, he was not yet quite dead
Now listen to the very last words the young pursuer said:

"I'm going to a better land, where everything is right
Where whiskey flows from telegraph poles, play poker every night
There's not a fucking thing to do but sit around and sing,
And chase the pretty poon-tang, o death where is thy sting?
O death where is thy sting? O death where is thy sting?
The bells of Hell may ring-a-ling-a-ling, for you but not for me.
O ring-a-ling, a-ring-ring, blow it out your ass,
O ring-a-ling, a-ring-ring, blow it out your ass,
O ring-a-ling, a-ring-ring, blow it out your ass,
Better days are coming by and by, o shit!"

Always Look At The Bright Side Of Life
Tune: Monty Python

Some things in life are bad;
They can really make you mad.
Other things just make you swear and curse.
When you're chewing on life's gristle,
Don't grumble, give a whistle!
And this'll help things turn out for the best…
And…
… always look on the bright side of life! (whistle)
Always look on the bright side of life…

If life seems jolly rotten,
There's something you've forgotten!
And that's to laugh and smile and dance and sing.
When you're feeling in the dumps,
Don't be silly chumps,
Just purse your lips and whistle -- that's the thing!

And... always look on the bright side of life... (whistle)
Always look on the bright side of life... (whistle)
For life is quite absurd,
And death's the final word.
You must always face the curtain with a bow!
Forget about your sin -- give the audience a grin,
Enjoy it -- it's the last chance anyhow!

So always look on the bright side of death!
Just before you draw your terminal breath.
Life's a piece of shit,
When you look at it.
Life's a laugh and death's a joke, it's true,
You'll see it's all a show,
Keep 'em laughing as you go.
Just remember that the last laugh is on you!

And always look on the bright side of life... (whistle)
Always look on the bright side of life... (whistle).

American Beer

Tune: American Pie

A long, long time ago
I can still remember how my first beer made me wanna die.
If I had any common sense
I would live in abstinance,
then maybe I'd be fit and satisfied.
But growing up was so much cooler
when the keg was that much fuller,
bad news in the toilet--
but nothing seemed to spoil it.
I can't remember how I chugged
Budweiser from a gallon jug,
and finished off another mug
the day I hit my stride.

Chorus:

So three cheers for American beer,
I can kill a keg of Miller or a case of Ranier,
let the Euro-trash laugh and ask themselves why,
but I'll drink it 'till the day that I die,
drink it 'till the day that I die.

Did you ever do a beer bong,
and guzzle it down 'till a liter's gone?
Just try that with Theakston's strong.
Oh, do you believe in warning labels,
or do you party when you're able,
and can you teach me how to dance on the table?
Well I know the English laugh at me
when they see me drinking MGD;
they say it's next to water,
but you can't chug bitter or porter!
I'm a yankee-doodle and I got no class
I drink beer from a plastic glass
but buddy, don't make me kick your ass
the day I hit my stride.

I started singing

Chorus:

Irishmen snicker and call it cute
when I throw a Michelob down the chute;
but I couldn't care the less.
Call us uncultured, call us boors,
call out for another round of Coors,
and when the beer muscles flex, we'll put you to the test--
Well I'd like to see you drink as many
liters of Guinness or Kilkenny
they may be darker and thicker,
but they can't top Schlitz Malt Liquor!
I have a taste for Irish stout, it's true,
but it's shyte to a can of Red, White, and Blue;
for pure ingestion nothing else will do
the day I hit my stride.

And there we were all in one place
a generation totally shit-faced,
but that's how it ought to be.
So Jack be nimble, Jack be quick,
Jack missed the toilet when he got sick

and when he returned, Jack got sick on me!
Well I know the Germans much prefer
their hefe-weizen and Munchener,
but you keep your bock and Paulaner
Ich bin ein Amerikaner!
They call me low-brow, barbarian, crude
to drink what Anheuser-Busch has brewed,
but oh, what medicine for the mood,
the day I hit my stride.

We went to a Belgian abbey with bibs on
and asked for a case of Pabst Blue Ribbon,
and the monks got most upset.
Pilferage, sacrilige, pass it around
then we shouted out for another round,
something I later came to regret--
Well, the brewing brothers got really pissed,
and made the sign of the cross with fists,
We all got up to fight,
oh, but we couldn't stand upright!
While the Belgians sipped their lambic ale,
the rest of us ended up in jail.
Do you recall who posted bail,
the day I hit my stride.

(slowly)
I met a girl who looked to me
a beer-inspired fantasy,
she just smiled and slapped my face.
So I stammered, staggered, start to stutter,
fell face-first into the gutter,
but the man there said to get out of his space.
And in the streets the bottles flew
the cops arrived and the lightweights spewed
but no one really watched us
they all passed out unconscious.
And the things I take for granted least--
barley, hops, and brewer's yeast--
will serve me up a liquid feast
the day I hit my stride.
And I'll be singing...

Three cheers for American beer,
I can kill a keg of Miller or a case of Ranier,
let the Europeans laugh and speculate why,
but I'll drink it 'till the day that I die,

drink it 'till the day that I die.

Angeles Pom-Pom Song

Have you ever been in the Philippines?
The place is full of Pom Pom Queens.
The clap is bad the siph is worse.
So flub you dub for safety first.

Chorus:

Singing rum and Coca-Cola, come down to Angeles.
Both mother and daughter, working for GI dollar.

The women with their dirty feet,
Walk up and down Angeles Street.
They come up close and whisper low,
"How about a little pom-pom, Joe?"

Chorus:

The Philippine pimp is very smart.
He gets his dough before you start.
The pom-pom there is very nice,
But twenty pesos is a helluva price.

Anthem Of The Royal Canadian Kilted Yaksmen

Ren & Stimpy

Our country reeks of trees,
Our yaks are really large,
And they smell like rotting beef carcasses.
And we have to clean-up after them,
And our saddle sores are the best.
We proudly wear women's clothing
And searing sand blows up our skirts.
And buzzards, they soar overhead
And poisonous snakes devour us whole,
Our bones will bleach in the sun.
And we will probably go to hell
And that is our great reward
For being the-uh-roy-yal
Canadian kilted yaksmen.

Ball Game

Tune: Take Me Out to the Ball Game

Whip it out at the ball game,
Wave it 'round at the crowd,
Dip it in jello and Crackerjack,
I don't care if you give it a whack,
'Cause it's--
Beat your meat at the ball game,
If you can't, whatta a shame,
For it's one, two,
And you're covered in goo,
At the old ball game!

Balad Of The Queen Berets

Tune: Ballad of the Green Berets

Falling fairies from the sky,
I broke a nail, Oh I could cry.
Don't you like how my tushy sways?
We are the fags of the Queen Berets.

Bill Clinton's words upon my ears,
"You fags have rights, be proud my dears."
I once was scared, now I'm okay,
Cause I'm a fag in the Queen Berets.

Put silver ear clips on my nuts,
I love the pain, now spank my butt.
The way you walk is awfully cute,
I sure would like to pack your chute!

This Army stuff is really slick,
Free meals and clothes and lots of dicks.
When I retire, I still get paid,
We thank you, Bill, from the Queen Berets.

Baghdad Betty

When you're baking in your khakis,
And you're just not having fun,
Cos you're staring at the 'raqis,

Down the barrel of a gun,
And Political Correctness,
Has your platoon on the run ...

She's sandy and she's sweaty
And they call her Baghdad Betty,
She'll do the whole platoon - so form a line,
She'll do them singly or in pairs,
(The latter gets you lower fares)
And can do them by the score to save you time.

When your gear is getting gritty,
In the blazing Basra heat,
And the food is getting shitty,
With just camels left to eat,
All the action's in Falluja ... hallelujah!
But you're looking for some action on the cheap.

She's sleazy and she's swell, aah!
And they call her Basra Bella,
She offers regiments a discount fee,
Be you soldier or deserter,
For small change she'll raise her burkha,
But she's starving so she'll do blow jobs for free.

When there's sand in your Big Whopper,
And you've camels in your tent,
Desert storms have grounded choppers,
And your Jeep has lost its paint,
The Camel Spiders are such monsters
That your sarge is feeling faint ...

But the soldiers have a matey,
She is called Karbala Katie,
Invade her sunni triangle tonight!
Overthrowing the dictator
Is a game we'll leave for later,
Cos Katie will go down without a fight.

[Slowly]
In heaven there are houris
Who will take away your worries,
Each day their maidenheads are grown anew.
We're not in heaven, we're in hell, eh?
We have Katie, Betty, Bella,
So until we get to heaven we'll make do!

Bang Bang Lulu

Chorus:

Bang Bang Lulu
Bangin' away all day
What'll we do for banging
When Lulu's gone away

Some girls work in factories
Some girls wok in stores
Lulu works behind a bar
With fifty other whores.

Wish I was a finger
On Lulu's little hand
Every time she wiped her ass
I'd see the promised land.

Lulu had a baby
She named it Sonny Jim
She threw it in the pisspot
To teach it how to swim.

Lulu had a baby
She had it on a rock
She couldn't call it Lulu
'Cause the bastard had a cock.

Last time I saw Lulu
I haven't seen her since
She was sucking of a combat pilot
Through a barbed wire fence.

Wish I was a piss pot
Under Lulu's bed
Every time she stooped to pee
I'd see her maidenhead.

Bestiality's Best

Tune: Tie Me Kangaroo Down, Boys

Chorus: Bestiality's best, boys,
Bestiality's best

Bestiality's best, boys,
Bestiality's best.

Tie me wallaby down, boys,
Tie me wallaby down,
You can't fuck him when he's jumping around, boys,
So tie me wallaby down.

Change your luck with a duck, Chuck,
Change your luck with a duck,
A duck's a marvellous fuck, Chuck,
So change your luck with a duck.

A drake's the best all around, mate,
A drake's the best all around,
Its entry's surrounded by down, mate,
A drake's the best all around.

A camel's a hell of a lay, Kay,
A camel's a hell of a lay,
Humping the hump, as they say, Kay,
A camel's a hell of a lay.

A moose is no bloody use, Bruce,
A moose is no bloody use,
She's big, she's mean, and she's loose, Bruce,
A moose is no bloody use.

You can shoot your load in a toad, dude,
You can shoot your load in a toad,
If there's nothing else to be rode, dude,
You can shoot your load in a toad.

Me wife was raped by an ape, Nate,
Me wife was raped by an ape,
She's in marvellous sexual shape, Nate,
Ever since she was raped by an ape.

A rhino's a hell of a treat, Pete,
A rhino's a hell of a treat,
The horniest thing on four feet, Pete,
A rhino's a hell of a treat.

A mongoose is no piece of cake, Jake,
A mongoose is no piece of cake,
He'll attack your one-eyed snake, Jake,

A mongoose is no piece of cake.

You can come again in a hen, men,
You can come again in a hen,
When you've had everything else in the pen, men,
You can come again in a hen.

I tried to roger a badger, boys,
I tried to roger a badger,
A badger's a hell of a dodger, boys,
You just can't roger a badger.

You can go the course on a horse, Morris,
You can go the course on a horse,
There's lots of animals worse, Morris,
You can go the course on a horse.
You can try your log in a frog, boys,
You can try your log in a frog,
If it's the only thing in the bog, boys,
You can try your log in a frog.

You can stick your pole in a mole, Cole,
You can stick your pole in a mole,
If your pole's incredibly small, Cole,
You can stick your pole in a mole.

You can try to screw a red 'roo, Lou,
You can try to screw a red 'roo,
Be careful it doesn't screw you, Lou,
When you try to screw a red 'roo.

An ostrich can give you a ride, Clyde,
An ostrich can give you a ride,
When you get your weapon inside, Clyde,
An ostrich's a real wild ride.

Screwing a turtle's a lark, Mark,
Screwing a turtle's a lark,
If you've got foreskin like bark, Mark,
Then screwing a turtle's a lark.

A gator is tricky to boff, Toff,
A gator is tricky to boff,
Wrong end and you'll get it bit off, Toff,
A gator is tricky to boff.

Any old beast for a fuck, Chuck,
Any old beast for a fuck,
Even an Irishman's luck, Chuck,
When you need a beast for a fuck.

Put your log up a dog, Claude,
Put your log up a dog,
Don't you fancy a dog, Claude,
Put your log up a dog, 'cause . . .

Big Bamboo

Tune: Working For the Yankee Dollar

I asked my lady what should I do,
To make her happy, not make her blue,
She said, "The only thing I want from you,
Is a little bitty of the big bamboo."

Chorus:

She wanted the big bamboo, bamboo,
Eye eye-eye eye-eye-eye,
Working for the Yankee dollar.

So I gave her a coconut,
She said, "I like him, he's okay,
But there's just one thing that worries me,
What good are the nuts without the tree?"

So I sold my lady a banana plant,
She said, "I like him, he's elegant,
We should not let him go to waste,
But he's much too soft to suit my taste."

So I bought my lady a sugar cane,
The fruit of fruits, I did explain,
But she was tired of him very quick,
She said, "I'd rather get my lips around your dip stick."

So I gave my honey a rambutan,
Soft and prickly, how the juices ran,
She said, "I've seen a fruit like this before,
But it had a long stalk and two pips in the core."
She met a chinaman, Him Hung Low,
They got married, went to Mexico,

But she divorced him very quick,
She said, "I want bamboo, not chopstick."

Big Strong Man

Have you heard about the big strong man?
He lives in a caravan
Have you heard about the Jeffrey Johnson fight?
Lord what a hell of a fight
Well you can take all the heavyweights you've got (what ye got?)
We got a lad who can beat the whole lot
He used to work here as a doorman
Now he's gonna fight the foreman

That's my brother, Sylvest (what's he got?)
A row of forty medals on his chest (big chest!)
He killed fifty barmen in the West
He knows no rest—bigger the man, hell's fire don't push (just shove)
Plenty o'room for you and me
He's got an arm like a leg (a lady's leg)
And a punch that would sink a battle ship (big ship!)
It takes all the army and the navy
To take the wind of Sylvest

Well, he thought he'd take a trip to Italy
He thought that he'd go by the sea
He jumped off the harbour in New York
And he swam like a man from Cork
He saw the Lusitania in distress (so what'd he do?)
He put the Lusitania on his chest (big chest!)
He drank all the water in the sea
And he walked all the way to Italy

That was my brother, Sylvest (what's he got?)
A row of forty medals on his chest (big chest!)
He killed fifty barmen in the West
He knows no rest—bigger the man, hell's fire don't push (just shove)
Plenty o'room for you and me
He's got an arm like a leg (a lady's leg)
And a punch that would sink a battle ship (big ship!)
It takes all the army and the navy
To take the bra off Mae West
Well, he thought he'd take a trip to old Japan
They turned out the whole brass band

He played every instrument they'd got—
Like a lad, sure he beat the whole lot!
Now the old church bells will ring (Hell's Bells!)
The old church choir will sing (Hell's Choir!)
They all turned out to say farewell,
To my big brother Sylvest.

That was my brother, Sylvest (what's he got?)
A row of forty medals on his chest (big chest!)
He killed fifty barmen in the West
He knows no rest—bigger the man, hell's fire don't push (just shove)
Plenty o'room for you and me
He's got an arm like a leg (a lady's leg)
And a punch that would sink a battle ship (big ship!)
It takes all the army and the navy
To take the wind of Sylvest

Birthday Song

Tune: Happy Birthday to You

Happy birthday, fuck you,
Happy birthday, fuck you,
Happy birthday, you asshole,
Happy birthday, fuck you.

Bitch A Dog

Tune: Do, Re, Mi

Bitch, a dog, a female dog,
Itch, a place for you to scratch,
Hitch, I pull my knickers up,
Grab, another word for snatch,
Bath, a place for making gin,
Sex, another word for sin,
Prick, a needle going in,
And that will bring us back to
Bitch, bitch, bitch, bitch . . .

Bondi Pier

I was down on Bondi Pier, sipping tubes of ice-cold beer
With a bucket full of prawns upon my knee

When I finished the last prawn, I had a technocolor yawn
And I chundered in the old Pacific Sea.

Chorus: Drink it up (drink it up, drink it up)
Bring it up (bring it up, bring it up)
Crack another dozen tubes of beer with me
If you want to throw your voice, mate you haven't any choice
But to chunder in the old Pacific Sea.

I was swimming through the surf when a mate of mine called Merv
Asked if he could have a tube or two with me
He had hardly finished it when he went for the big spit
And he chundered in the old Pacific Sea.

I've had liquid laughs in bars, and I've hurled from moving cars
And I've chundered where and when it suited me
But if I had to choose the spot to regurgitate the lot
Then I'd chunder in the old Pacific Sea.

Bone Drivers Eat Pussy !!!

Cielito Lindo

Chorus:

Oh, Aye, Aye, Aye, Aye

1st- Bone Drivers eat PUSSY!!!
2nd- Your mother swims out to meet troop ships
3rd- Your sister sucks bat shit off cave walls
4th- Your grandmother douches with Drano
5th- Your grandmother licks moose come off pinecones
6th- Your mother does squat thrusts on fire plugs
7th- Your father refills cream donuts
8th- Your mother goes down on Iraqis
9th- Your brother beats off in confession
10th- Your cousin just butt-fucked a collie
11th- Your mother sucks farts from dead seagulls
12th- Your sister blows goats for a quarter
13th- Your uncle eats lunch at the sperm bank
14th- Your sister's best friend is a carrot
15th- Your sister gives hand jobs to camels
16th- You can't say FUCK at the O'Club

So sing me another verse,
That's worse than the other verse

And waltz me around by my Willy!

Verses:
There was a young man from Boston
Who traded his car for an Austin.
There was room for his ass and a gallon of gas
But his ball hung out and he lost them.

There was a young man from Nantucket,
Whose dick was so long he could suck it.
He said with a grin, as he wiped off his chin,
If my ear were a cunt, I would fuck it.

There once was a young man from Kent,
Whose dick was so long it was bent.
To stay out of trouble, he stuck it in double,'
Instead of coming, he went.

There once was a young girl named Alice,
Who used a dynamite stick for a phallus.
They found her vagina in South Carolina,
And a piece of her hymen in Dallas.

There was a professor from the Mall,
Who possessed a hexahydroginal ball.
The square root of it's weight, plus his pecker times eight,
Was four-fifths of five-eighths of fuck all.

There once was girl from France,
Who boarded a train by chance.
The engineer fucked her, so'd the conductor,
And the brakeman went off in his pants.

There once was a man from Bombay,
Who fashioned a cunt out of clay.
The heat of his prick, turned the clay into brick,
And rubbed all his foreskin away.

There once was a girl named Gail,
Between her tits was the price of her tail.
And on her behind, for the sake of the blind,
Was the same information in Brialle.

There once was a young man from Dakota,
Who wouldn't pay a whore what he owed her.
So with great savoir faire, she climbed on a chair,

And pissed in his whiskey and soda.

There once was a pilot named Paul,
Who's cock was the longest of all.
This appendage of his got him into showbiz,
With a royal performance on call.

Now Paul found there's trouble in fame,
Every whore in the ville knew his name.
And their unhidden fear, of his fantastic gear,
Put a halt to old Paul's favorite game.

Now in hopes of relief to Seoul he went,
Our pilot Paul, with his dick bent.
And though folded in half, the whores still feared his shaft,
'Cause the bend in his tool made a dent.

In Pusan, with a girl to his taste,
Paul dropped his drawers and entered in haste.
But he didn't unfold when he entered her hole,
And he spilled his whole WAD, "what a waste."

There once was a Captain named Tuck,
Who went to the ville for a fuck.
He spread open her legs, found ten cockroach eggs,
Three boogers, some scabs, and green muck.

Now later when Tuck wiped his chin,
He smiled and said with a grin.
"Didn't take her to heart till she sprayed our a fart,
That tasted like birdshit and gin."

A combat pilot named Tucker,
Said, while instructing a novice cocksucker.
Don't puff 'em out like you're blowing your snout,
Be gentle and work with a pucker.

Oh, the Romans had great spacious halls,
In which they geld great sexual brawls.
Which would last, so they say, for a week and a day,
There's no doubt those bastards had balls.

There once was a pilot from the sticks,
Who didn't like cunts, only dicks.
He told MPC, "find a place for me",
Now he's one of the boys who checks six.

There once was a man from Vancouver,
Who thought he knew every maneuver.
'Till a girl from Van Nuys gave him a rise,
With the aid of a portable Hoover.

A handsome young plumber named McGee,
Was plumbing his girl by the sea.
When all of a sudden, she said, "Quick, someone's coming",
Tee Hee, said McGee, It's me.

There was a young lady from Wheeling,
Who had a peculiar feeling.
She laid on her back, and tickled her crack,
And pissed all over the ceiling.

There once was young girl from Peru,
Who said as the Bishop withdrew.
The Vicar is quicker, he's also a licker,
And he's considerably thicker than you.

There was a young lass named Alice,
Who pissed in the Archbishop's chalice.
It was not from relief, as was the belief,
But purely from Protestant malice.

There once was a young girl named Myrtle,
Who was raped on the beach by a turtle.
The result of the fuck, was two eggs and a duck,
Which proved the turtle was fertile.

There once was a young girl from the Azores,
Whose cunt was all covered in sores.
The dogs in the street, wouldn't eat the green meat,
That hung in festoons from her drawers.

There once was a young couple named Kelly,
Who used Vaseline petroleum jelly.
But once in their haste, they used library paste,
And now they're stuck belly to belly.

There once was a pirate named Bates,
Who was learning to rumba on skates.
He fell on his Cutlass, rendering him nutless,
And practically useless on dates.

There was a young lady named Esther,
Who said to the man who undressed her.
"If you don't mind, use the hole from behind,
The one in front is beginning to fester."

Bonnie Lass Of Fyfie

There once was a troop of Irish dragoons
Come marching down thru Fyfie, O
And the captain feel in love with a very bonnie lass
And the name she was called was pretty Peggy-o
Chorus: O come down the stairs, Pretty Peggy, my dear
Come down the stairs, Pretty Peggy-o
Come down the stairs, comb back your yellow hair
Bid a last farewell to your mammy-o

There's many a bonnie lass in the glen of Auchterlass
There's many a bonnie lass in Gairioch-o
There's many a bonnie Jean in the streets of Aberdeen
But the flower of them all lives in Fyvie, O

It's braw, aye it's braw, a captain's lady for to be
And it's braw to be a captain's lady-o
It's braw to ride around and to follow the camp
And to ride when your captain he is ready-o

O I'll give you ribbons, love, and I'll give you rings
I'll give you a necklace of amber-o
I'll give you a silken petticoat with flounces to the knee
If you'll convey me doon to your chamber-o

I never did intend a soldier's lady for to be
A soldier never shall enjoy me-o
I never did intend to gae tae a foreign land
A soldier never will I marry-o

I'll drink nae more o your claret wine
I'll drink nae more o your glasses-o
Tomorrow is the day when we maun ride away
So farewell tae your Fyvie lasses-o

The colonel he cried, mount, mount, boys, mount
The captain, he cried, we'll tarry-o
O tarry yet a while, just another day or twa

Til I see if the bonnie lass will marry-o

Twas in the early morning, when we marched awa
And O but the captain he was sorry-o
The drums they did beat a merry brasselgeicht
And the band played the bonnie lass of Fyvie, O

Long ere we came to the glen of Auchterlass
We had our captain to carry-o
And long ere we won into the streets of Aberdeen
We had our captain to bury-o

Green grow the birks on bonnie Ethanside
And low lie the lowlands of Fyvie, O
The captain's name was Tuck and he died for a maid
He died for the bonny lass of Fyvie, O

Boom, Oooh, Yakatata

Tune: Will You Kiss Me Tonight

Chorus:

(continuously): Boom, oooh, yakatata

Will you miss me tonight when I'm gone?
Will you go to bed with your see-through nightie on?
Will you reach out for your little plastic friend,
Put some baby oil around it's throbbing end?
Will you spare a thought for me while I'm gone?
Will you laugh with your friend over which is long?
Will you slide it up your thighs and up to your crack,
Smile to yourself, Thank God he's not back?
Will you miss me tonight when I'm gone?
'Cause the batteries in your friend have almost gone,
And you never could make that charger thing come on?
So now you'll miss me tonight 'cause I'm gone, try a banana,
'Cause you'll miss me tonight 'cause I'm gone,
Ya bitch.

Botany Bay

Me name is Pat O'Leary,
I'm a navvy lad from Cork,
Me boss he is a nicker,

And I'm sick of his piecework.
I'll sail to dear Australia,
A land so far away.
So that's my fate, I'm goin' to emigrate
To the shores of Botany Bay.

Chorus:

Farewell to your bricks and mortar,
Farewell to your dirty lies,
Farewell to your gangways and your gangplanks
And to hell with your overtime.
For the good ship Ragamuffin,
She's lying at the Quay
For to take oul' Pat with the shovel on his back
To the shores of Botany Bay.

I'm on my way down to the Quay
Where the ship at anchor lays,
To command a gang of navvies
That they told me to engage.
I thought I drop in for a drink
Before I went away,
For to take a trip on an emigrant ship
To the shores of Botany Bay.

The boss came up this morning,
He says "Well pat, you know,
If you don't get your navvies out
I'm afraid you'll have to go".
So I asked him for me wages,
And demanded all me pay,
For I told him straight, I'm going to emigrate
To the shores of Botany Bay.

And when I reach Australia,
I'll go and look for gold.
Ther's plenty there for digging off
Or so I have been told.
Or else I'll go back to me trade
And a hundred brick I'll lay,
Because I live for an eight hour shift
On the shores of Botany Bay.

Bulldog On The Bank

Oh the bulldog on the bank, and the bullfrog in the pool,
Oh the bulldog on the bank, and the bullfrog in the pool,
Oh the bulldog on the bank, and the bullfrog in the pool.
Oh the bulldog called the bullfrog a green ol' water fool.

Singing (Yodel) idle, idle, idley ideooo
Singing (Yodel) idle, idle, idley ideooo
Singing (Yodel) idle, idle, idley ideooo

Pharaoh's daughter on the bank, little Moses in the pool,
Pharaoh's daughter on the bank, little Moses in the pool,
Pharaoh's daughter on the bank, little Moses in the pool.
She fished him out with a telegraph pole and sent him off to school

Singing (Yodel) idle, idle, idley ideooo
Singing (Yodel) idle, idle, idley ideooo
Singing (Yodel) idle, idle, idley ideooo.

Bullshit In The Box

Tune: Whiskey in the Jar

'Twas early Friday evening as I left work to travel
I met with Colonel Davis and my weekend plans unraveled.
He first produced me orders, and then produced a warning,
saying, "Pack up your gear, because you're leaving in the morning."

Chorus:

Desert Fox, Southern Watch, Allied Force,
whack fol Delib'rate Guard,
whack fol Delib'rate Guard,
there's bullshit in the in-box.

I gathered up my courage to sway the man to save us,
I could've turned a Bolshevik but oh not Colonel Davis.
I sighed, and I swore that I shouldn't be forsaken;
he didn't like my reasons, so to Al Kharj I was taken.

If there's anyone can save me I'm sure he'd be civilian,
and would that I were one of them and make myself a million.
I'd like to join their number, with some transition assistance,
but I'm stuck here on AEF at my DO's insistance.

If I be told to handle just one more worthless mission
the devil take my job, I'd let him have it for the pissin'.
But I'll not be a traitor, and nor I'll be shirker--
I'll bite my tongue and bide my time 'till I'm a postal worker!

Buy Us A Drink

Buy us a drink and we'll sing you a song
of the chances you missed, and the love that went wrong.
If you can't buy whiskey, stand us a pint,
And we'll lug'er strait down, and we'll sing half the night.
Lug'er down,
Lug'er down.
As long as there's light in the day,
For you'll get no more sup, when you're number is up,
And they lay you to rot in the grave.
There's girls in the parlours, there's girls in the bars.
They paint on the smiles, so you don't see the scars.
They get lots of offers, but not much respect
For raising three kids on a government cheque.

By The Light

By the light, SSH, SSH, SSH--SSH, SSH, SSH
Of the flickering match, SSH, SSH, SSH--SSH, SSH, SSH
I saw her snatch, SSH, SSH, SSH--SSH, SSH, SSH
In a watermelon patch, Oh yeah.
By the light, SSH, SSH, SSH--SSH, SSH, SSH
Of the flickering match, SSH, SSH, SSH--SSH, SSH, SSH
I saw her gleam,
I heard her scream,
You are burning my snatch, SSH, SSH, SSH--SSH, SSH, SSH
Oh daughter, dear daughter, don't you be sad.
It was the same trouble I had with your dad.
There's many a man who will come to the call,
Of the wife of a man who has no balls at all.

The daughter went home, took her mother's advice.
And found the results exceedingly nice.
A bouncing young baby was born in the fall,
To the wife of a man who had no balls at all.

Bye, Bye, Cherry

Tune: Bye Bye Blackbird

Back your ass against the wall,
Here I come, balls and all,
Bye, bye, cherry!
Won't your mother be disgusted,
When she finds your cherry's busted,
Bye, bye, cherry!
Wrap your legs around a little tighter,
I can feel my load is getting lighter,
Shake your ass and wiggle your tits,
Till my little pecker spits,
Cherry, bye bye!

Cats On The Rooftop

Tune: Do Ye Ken John Peel

The donkey is a solitary moke,
He very seldom gets a poke;
But when he does, he lets it soak,
As he revels in the joys of copulation.

Chorus:

Cats on the roof tops, cats on the tiles,
Cats with syphilis, cats with piles,
Cats with their arseholes wreathed in smiles
As they revel in the joys of copulation.

The dainty little skylark sings a very pretty song,
He has a ponderous penis fully forty cubits long,
You should hear his high crescendo, when his mate is on the prong,
As he revels in the joys of fornication.

The whale is a mammal, as everybody knows,
He takes two days to have a shag, but when he's in the throes,
He doesn't stop to take it out; he piddles through his nose,
As he revels in the joys of fornication.

The poor old rhinoceros, so it appears,
Never gets a grind in a thousand years,
But when he does, he makes up for arrears,
As he revels in the joys of fornication.

In Egypt's sunny clime, the crocodile,
Gets a flip only once in a while,
But when he does, it floods the Nile,
As he revels in the joys of fornication.

Now a funny old fish is the old sperm whale,
With a funny little diddle tucked beneath his tail,
And he rides his missus in the teeth of a gale,
As he revels in the joys of fornication.

Little Mary Johnson will be seven next July,
She's never had a naughty, but she thought she'd like to try,
So she took her daddy's walking stick and did it on the sly,
As she reveled in the joys of fornication.

Long-legged curates grind like goats,
Pale-faced spinsters shag like shoats,
And the whole damn world stands about and gloats,
As they revel in the joys of fornication.

The ostrich in the desert is a solitary chick,
Without the opportunity to dip its wick,
But whenever it does, it slips in thick,
As he revels in the joys of fornication.

The ape is small and rather slow,
Erect he stands a foot or so,
So when he comes it's time to go,
As he revels in the joys of fornication.

The flea disports among the trees,
And there consorts with whom he please,
To fill the land with bastard fleas,
As he revels in the joys of fornication.

The elephant's prong is big and round,
A small one scales a thousand pound,
Two together rock the ground,
As they revel in the joys of fornication.

The camel likes to have his fun,
His night is made when he is done,
He always gets two humps for one,
As he revels in the joys of fornication.

The orangutan is a colorful sight,

There's a glow on its ass like a pilot light,
As it jumps and it leaps in the night,
As it revels in the joys of fornication.

The oyster is a paragon of purity,
And you can't tell the he from the she,
But he can tell and so can she,
As they revel in the joys of fornication.

A thousand verses all in rhyme,
To sit and sing them seems a crime,
When we could better spend our time,
Reveling in the joys of fornication.

When you find yourself in springtime with a surge of sexual joy,
And your wife has got the rag on and your daughter's rather coy,
Then jam it up the backside of your favorite choirboy,
As you revel in a smooth ejaculation.

The Regimental Sergeant Major leads a miserable life,
He can't afford a mistress and he doesn't have a wife,
So he puts it up the bottom of the Regimental Fife,
As he revels in the joys of fornication.

The hippopotamus so it seems,
Very seldom has wet dreams;
But when he does it comes in streams,
As he revels in the joys of copulation.

The Australian lady emu when she wants to find a mate,
Wanders round the desert with a feather up her date,
You should see that feather, when she meets her destined fate,
As she revels in the joys of fornication.

The poor domestic doggie, on his chain all day,
Never gets a chance to get himself a lay,
So he licks himself in a frantic way,
As he revels in the joys of fornication.

Poor old bovine, poor old bull,
Very seldom gets a pull;
But when he does, the cow is full,
As he revels in the joys of copulation.

Poor little tortoise in his shell,
Doesn't manage very well;

But when he does he fucks like hell,
As he revels in the joys of copulation.

Now the hairy old gorilla is a sedentary ape,
Who very seldom does much rape;
But when he does he comes like tape,
As he revels in the joys of copulation.

When you wake up in the morning with your penis in your hand,
And you have a funny feeling in your seminary gland;
If you cannot get a woman, try to get a clean old man,
As you revel in the joys of copulation.

Now I met a young girl who had a great rear,
But gave me a dose of gonorrhoea;
Fools rush in where angels fear
To revel in the joys of copulation.

Charlie for The MTA

Let me tell you a story of a man named Charlie
On this tragic and fateful day
He put ten cents in his pocket, kissed his wife and his children,
Went to work on the MTA.

Chorus:

Did he ever return? NO, HE NEVER RETURNED
And his fate is still unlearned... BULLSHIT!
He may ride forever 'neath the streets of Boston,
He's the man who never returned.

Charlie handed in his dime at the Kendall Square Station
And he changed for Jamaica Plain.
When he got off the conductor said, "One more nickel,"
Charlie couldn't get off that train.

Now all night long Charlie rode through the tunnel
Saying, "What will become of me?
Will I ever again see my sister in Chelsea
Or my cousin back in Roxbury?"

Charlie's wife goes down to the Scollay Square Station
Every day at quarter past two,
And standing on the platform she gives Charlie the finger
As the train goes rolling through.

Now you citizens of Boston, don't you think it's a scandal
That the people have to pay and pay,
Fight the fair increase, vote for George O'Brien,
Get poor Charlie off the MTA!

Christopher Robin

Tune: Christopher Robin

Little boy kneels at the foot of the stairs,
Clutched in his hands is a tuft of white hairs,
Oh, my, just fancy that,
Christopher Robin castrated the cat.

Little boy kneels at the foot of the bed,
Lily-white hands are caressing his head,
Oh, my, couldn't be worse,
Christopher Robin is fucking his nurse.

Little boy sits on the lavatory pan,
Gently caressing his little old man,
Flip, flop, into the tank,
Christopher Robin is having a yank.

Cigarettes, Whisky and Wild, Wild Woman

Chorus:

Cigarettes, whiskey and wild, wild women
They'll drive you crazy, they'll drive you insane;
Cigarettes, whiskey and wild, wild women
They'll drive you crazy, they'll drive you insane

Once I was happy and had a good wife
I had enough money to last me for life
Then I met with a gal and we went on a spree
She taught me smokin' and drinkin' whiskey

Cigarettes are a blight on the whole human race
A man is a monkey with one in his face;
Take warning dear friend, take warning dear brother
A fire's on one end, a fools on the t'other.

And now good people, I'm broken with faith

The lines on my face make a well written page
I'm weavin' this story -- how sadly but true
On women and whiskey and what they can do

Wild the cross at the head of my grave
For women and whiskey here lies a poor slave.
Take warnin' poor stranger, take warnin' dear friend
In wide clear letters this tale of my end.

Cock Robin

Tune: Who Killed Cock Robin

Who killed cock robin?
"I," said the sparrow,
"With my bow and arrow,
I killed cock robin."

Chorus: (words & actions):
Oh-h-h-h the birds of the air said,
Fuck it! Let's chuck it!
When they heard cock robin
Had kicked the fucking bucket!
When they heard-d-d-d cock robin-n-n-n
Had kicked the fucking bucket!

Who saw him die?
"I," said the fly,
"With my little eye,
I saw him die."

Who'll take his blood?
"I," said the mole,
"With my little bowl,
I'll take his blood."

Who'll dig his grave?
"I," said the owl,
"With my little trowel,
I'll dig the grave."

Who'll ring the bell?
"I," said the bull,
"With my mighty tool,
I'll ring the bell."

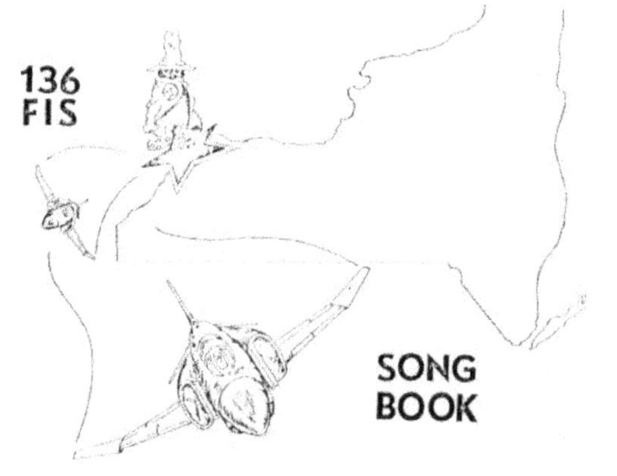

Who'll say the prayer?
"I," said the rook,
"With my little book,
I'll say the prayer."

Columbo

Tune: Columbus Sailed the Ocean Blue

In Fourteen Hundred and Ninety-Two,
A schoolboy from I-taly,
Walked the streets of ancient Rome,
And jacked off in the alley.

Chorus:

He knew the world was round, oh,
He knew it could be found, oh,
That mathematical, geographical,
Son of a bitch, Columbo.

Columbo went to the Queen of Spain,
And asked for ships and cargo,
He said he'd kiss the royal ass,
If he didn't bring back Chicago.

Now three slick ships set out to sea,
Each one a double-decker,
The queen she waved her handkerchief,
Columbo waved his pecker.

The sailors on Columbo's ship,
Had each his private knothole,
But Columbo was a superman,
And used a padded porthole.

Colombo came upon the deck,
His cock was like a flagpole,
He grabbed the bo'sun by the neck,
And shoved it up his asshole.

Columbo had a one-eyed cat,
He kept it in the cabin,
He rubbed its ass with axle grease,
And started in a-jabbin'.

Alconbury -CD

Columbo had a first mate,
He loved him like a brother,
Every night in the pale moonlight
They buggered one another.

For forty days and forty nights,
They sailed the broad Atlantic.
Columbo and his scurvy crew,
For want of a piece were frantic.

They spied a whore upon the shore,
And off came shirts and collars,
In twenty minutes by the clock,
She'd made ten thousand dollars.

With a joyful shout they ran about,
And practiced fornication,
When they sailed they left behind,
Ten times the population.

And when his men pulled out again,
To take their homeward trip up,
They'd caught the pox from every box,
And syphilized all Europe.

Columbo went in haste to the Queen,
Because it was his duty,
He gave to her a dose of clap,
He had no other booty.

So she threw him in a stinking jail,
And left him there to grumble,
A ball and chain tied to his balls,
So ended poor Columbo.

Come Sit On My Face, If You Love Me

Tune: Red River Valley

Come and sit on my face, if you love me,
Come and sit on my face, if you care,
And I'll drink from your Red River Valley,
And munch on your curly pubic hairs.

Oh, if I had the wings of an eagle,

And the balls of a hairy baboon,
I would fly to the ends of creation,
And I'd butt-fuck the Man in the Moon.

Oh, take it in the hand, Mrs Murphy,
It feels just like a rolling pin.
But if you roll it between your hands,
It'll take some time to be useful again.

Oh, take it in the mouth, Mrs Murphy,
It only weighs a quarter of a pound.
It's got hairs round its neck like a turkey,
And it spits when you shake it up and down.

Oh, take it between the breasts, Mrs Murphy,
And look it staight in its one eye.
It will lie at peace between your bosom,
Until finally milk-tears you cry.

Oh, place it between your legs, Mrs Murphy,
It is just aching to crawl inside.
It has a helmet on its head like a soldier,
And it will shoot all its ammo, then die.
Oh, but never touch (name), Mrs Murphy,
It seems his is covered with scabs.
His has warts all over like a horny toad,
And is protected by an army of crabs.

Danny Boy

Oh Danny boy, the pipes, the pipes are calling,
From glen to glen, and down the mountain side.
The summer's gone, and all the roses falling,
It's you, it's you must go, and I must bide!

But come ye back when summer's in the meadow
Or when the valley's hushed and white with snow
Oh, come ye back, in sunshine or in shadow
Oh, Danny boy, oh, Danny boy, I love you so.

And if you come when all the flowers are dying
And I am dead, as dead I well may be
You'll come and find the place where I am lying
And kneel and say an "Ave" there for me.

And I shall hear, tho soft you tread above me
And all my dreams will warmer, sweeter be
If you'll not fail to tell me that you love me
I'll sleep in peace, until you come to me!

Death March

"Oh dear", said the landlord, so he turned his colour telly on,
"Another fatal accident, the third this week I fear.
If they can't hold there own, why don't they stay at home,
My God we don't half get some funny customers in here."

Dinah

Chorus:

Dinah, Dinah, show us your leg,
Show us your leg, show us your leg,
Dinah, Dinah, show us your leg,
A yard above your knee.

I wish I were the diamond ring,
On Dinah's dainty hand,
Then, every time she wiped her ass,
I'd see the promised LAND, LAND, LAND!

The rich girl rides a limousine,
The poor girl rides a truck,
But the only ride that Dinah has,
Is when she has a RIGHT GOOD FUCK!

The rich girl uses a sanitary towel,
The poor girl uses a sheet,
But Dinah uses nothing at all,
Leaves a trail along the STREET, STREET, STREET!

The rich girl wears a ring of gold,
The poor girl one of brass,
But the only ring that Dinah wears,
Is the one around her ASS, ASS, ASS!

The rich girl wears a brassiere,
The poor girl uses string,
But Dinah uses nothing at all,

She lets the bastards SWING, SWING, SWING!

The rich girl uses Vaseline,
The poor girl uses lard,
But Dinah uses axle grease,
Because her cunt's so HARD, HARD, HARD!

The rich girl works in factories,
The poor girl works in stores,
But Dinah works in a honky-tonk,
With forty other WHORES, WHORES, WHORES!

Do Virgins Taste Better ?

Tune: The Irish Washerwoman

A dragon has come to our village today,
We've asked him to leave, but he won't go away.
He's talked to our king and they worked out a deal,
No homes will he burn and no crops will he steal.

Now there is but one catch, we dislike it a bunch,
Twice a year he invites him a virgin to lunch.
We've no other choice, so the deal we'll respect,
But we can't help but wonder and pause to reflect.
Chorus:

Do virgins taste better than those who are not?
Are they salty, or sweeter, more juicy or what?
Do you savor them slow? Gulp them down on the spot?
Do virgins taste better than those who are not?

Now we'd like to be shed you, and many have tried.
But no one can get thru your thick scaly hide.
We hope that some day, some brave knight will come by.
'Cause we can't wait around 'til you're too fat to fly.

You've impeccable taste in your women for sure,
They always are pretty, they always are pure.
But your notion of dining, it makes us all flinch,
For your favorite entree is barbecued wench.

Now we've found a solution, it works out so neat,
If you insist on nothing but virgins to eat.
No more will our number ever grow small,
We'll simply make sure there's no virgins at all!

Do Your Balls Hang Low?

Tune: Sailor's Hornpipe

Chorus:

Ting-a-ling, God damn, find a woman if you can.
If you can't find a woman, find a clean old man.
If you're ever in Gibraltar, take a flying fuck at Walter.
Can you do the double shuffle when your balls hang low?

Do your balls hang low? Do they swing to and fro?
Can you tie 'em in a knot? Can you tie 'em in a bow?
Can you throw 'em on your shoulder like a European soldier?
Can you do the double shuffle when your balls hang low?

Other verses:
Do they make a lusty clamor when you hit 'em with a hammer?
Can you bounce 'em off the wall like an Indian rubber ball?
Do they have a hollow sound when you drag 'em on the ground?
Do you feel a mellow tingle when you hit 'em with a shingle?
Do they squeal like dogs when you tromp 'em with your clogs?
Do they have a salty taste when you wrap 'em round your waist?
Do they chime like a gong when you pull upon your dong?

Early One Evening

Early one evening, just as the pubs were opening,
A traveller came walking down a dark and rainy street.
He saw a door ajar, went into the public bar,
"Landlord I would like a pint and something good to eat."

"I fancy some crusty bread, and roast beef of old England,
Butter from the churn and tangy home made pickle too,
And if you think you could Draw some bitter from the wood,
I'd be most content to quaff a foaming pint or two."

"I'll sit by your fireside and contemplate the infinite,
The quiet of your hostelry shall seep into my heart,
And should a regular Venture into the bar,
Perhaps I might engage him in a contest at the darts."

"Come in", said the landlord, "I've got pre-packed fish paste sandwiches,
A soya sausage substitute I purchase by the ton,
And if you fancy it, I could defrost a bit,

And plaster it in ketchup in a supermarket bun."

"I'll pull you a foaming pint of Super Sparkle Readi-Bru,
As advertised on telly by a famous rugby scrum,
No filthy barrels here, we serve hygienic beer,
Safely pasteurized inside an aluminium drum."

"Sit down by the fire squire I'll switch the logs on right away,
Perhaps you'd like a gamble on my latest fruit machine,
Three cherries in a row, that should set your heart aglow,
Or how about my jukebox, that should really set the scene."

The traveller sat down beside the polystyrene inglenook,
The plastic beams vibrating to the electronic sound,
Took a bite - began to chew, sank his pint of Readi-Bru,
Gave a ghastly gurgle...[UUURGH]...and fell dead upon the ground....

Finnigan's Wake

Tim Finnigan lived on Walker Street
A gentle Irishman, mighty odd
He'd a beautiful brogue so rich and sweet
And to rise in the world he carried a hod
You see he'd sort of a tipplin' way
With a love for the liquor poor Tim was born
To help him on with his work each day
He'd a drop of the creatur every morn.

Chorus:

Whack for the da' now dance to your partner
Round the floor your trotter's shake
Wasn't it the truth I told you
Lot's o' fun at Finnigan's wake.

One morning Tim was rather full
His head felt heavy which made him shake
He fell from the ladder and he broke his skull
So they carried him home his corpse to wake
They rolled him up in a nice clean sheet
They laid him out upon the bed
With a gallon of whiskey at his feet
And a barrel of porter at his head.

His friends assembled at the wake

And Mrs. Finnigan called for lunch
First they brought in tea and cake,
Then pipe tobacco and whiskey punch
Biddie O'Brien began to cry,
"Such a nice clean corpse did you ever see
Aye Tim, mavourneen, why did ya die?"
"Ah, hold your gob!" says Paddie McGee.

Then Biddie O'Connor took up the job
"Oh, Biddie," says she, "You're wrong I'm sure."
Biddie gave her a belt in the gob
And she left her sprawlin' on the floor
Then the war did soon engage
Twas woman to woman and man to man
Shillelagh-law was all the rage
And the row and eruption soon began.

Then Micky Maloney raised his head
When a noggin of whiskey flew at him
It missed him fallin' on the bed
The liquor scattered over Tim
Tom revives see how he rises
Timothy risin' from the bed
Sayin' "Whirl your whiskey round like blazes!
Thanum an Diall! Did you think I'm dead?"

Fornication - Masturbation

Tune: Alouette)

Chorus:

Fornication, I love fornication,
Fornication, how I love to fuck.

Leader: How I like to be on top,
Pack: Yes, he likes to be on top
Leader: Be on top,
Pack: Be on top,
Leader: Fornicate,
Pack: Fornicate,

Leader is now the next person on the right-lead goes around the circle with each new verse, and all old verses should be repeated, as in AAHLAWETA:

Other verses:
How I like it standing up
How I like to hide the salami
Bury the bone
Poke the hay
Slice the slit
Drive it deep
Ride the baloney pony
Bump and grind
Pump and hump
Grind her mound
How I like harpooning clams
Spear the snatch
Cleave the quim
Give jungle love
etc . . .

This goes on until no one can think of new fornication verses, at which point the song becomes "Masturbation":

Chorus:
Masturbation, I love masturbation,
Masturbation, I love to masturbate.

Leader: How I like to choke my chicken,
Pack: Yes, he likes to choke his chicken,
Leader: Choke my chicken,
Pack: Choke his chicken,
Leader: Masturbate,
Pack: Masturbate,

Chorus:

Other verses:
Spank my monkey
Lope my mule
Rub my nub
Whip my lizard
Pound the pud
Flog my log
Beat my meat
Pull my pony
Walk the weenie
Yank my chain
Wrestle Cyclops
Corral the tadpoles

Crown the bishop
Shake Jake the one-eyed snake

Fuck The Giant Penis

Tune: Puff the Magic Dragon

Once a pure white virgin lived by the sea,
She frolicked o'er pastoral fields, her name Virginity,
A sweet young lass of just sixteen, a rosebud ripe and firm,
She wandered o'er the verdant hills, not knowing of the sperm.

Well, Fuck the Giant Penis lived not far away,
His cock was damn near two feet long; he poked one twice a day,
He was an Ivy Leaguer with vest and pinstriped suit,
He drove a roadster XKE, the sexed-up extrovert.

One day while he was reaming around the rural strips,
He spied her picking flowers there, that lass with swinging hips,
He jumped out of the driver's seat and grabbed her by the ass,
He tore off all her clothing, and laid her in the grass.

Her maidenhead was busted, the ground ran bloody red,
He poked her till the twilight came, then took her home to bed,
He poked her till the sun rose, she begged for more and more,
He turned that pure virginity into a God damned whore.

Fighter Pilots Eat Pussy

Chorus:
Oh, Aye, Yi, Yi

Option 2

So lets have another verse
that's worse than the other verse
and Waltz me around by my Willie

I got gonorrhea
From Fucking Maria

1. Fighter pilots eat pussy (and love it)
2. Taco's never eat pussy-Bullshit!
3. Your mother swims after troop ships(and catches them)
4. Your sister eats batshit off cavewalls
5. Your Grandmother douches with draino
6. In college they called your dad butt-fuck
7. Your mother licks moose cum off pine cones
8. Your mother does squat thrusts on fire plugs
9. Your sister's in love with a carrot.
10. In China they do it for chile

There once was a young lady named Alice
who used a dynamite stick for a phallus
they found her vagina in North Carolina
And parts of her ass in Dallas

There once was a young lady from France
Who hopped on a train in a trance
The engineer fucked her before the conductor
And the brakeman got off in his pants

There once was a man of class
Who's balls were made from brass
When they swung together,
they played stormy weather
And lightning shot out of his ass

There once was a young man from kildair
Who buggered his girl on the stairs
The bannister broke, he doubled the stroke
And finished her off in mid-air

There once was a man from Rangoon
Who was born by the light of the moon
He had not the luck, to be born by a fuck
But was a wet dream scooped up in a spoon

In the garden of eden sat Adam
With his hand on the butt of his madam
He chuckled with mirth, for he knew on this Earth
There were only two balls and he had 'em

There was an old hermit named Dave
Who kept a dead Whore in his cave
He said I'll admit, I'm a bit of a shit
But think of the money I'll save

There once was a harlet named Jones
Who had no erogenous zones
When her efforts to fake, could not fool
even Jake
She decided to try some Whore-moans

There once was a man from Nantucket
Who's dick was so long he could suck it
He said with a grin, as he wiped off his chin
"If my ear were a cunt I would fuck it."

There once was a young man from Kent
Whose prick was so long it bent
To save himself the trouble, he stuck it
in double
And instead of coming he went

A queer who lived in Khartoum
took a lesbian up to his room
They argued all night, over who had the right
To do what, and with what, and to whom

There once was a farmer named Fritz
Who planted an acre of tits
They came up in the fall, pink nipples and all
And he literally chewed them to bits

An Argentine gaucho named Bruno
Said fucking is one thing that I do know
All women are fine, and sheep are divine
But llamas are numero uno

There was a young lady from Decatur
Who screwed a big alligator
Nobody knew the results of the screw
Cause after he laid her he ate her

There once was a man from New Brighton
Who said my dear you've a tight one
She said oh my soul, you have the wrong hole
It's up in the front that's the right one

There was a professor from the mall
Who had a hexahydroginal ball
The square of it's weight, plus his pecker times eight
Was four/fifths of five eights of fuck all

There once was a man from Bombay
Who fashioned a cunt out of clay
The heat of his prick turned the clay into brick
And rubbed all his foreskin away

There once was a lady named Lil
Who swallowed an atomic pill
They found her vagina in North Carolina
And one of her tits in Brazil

There once was a man from Rangoon
Who's farts could be heard to the moon
They'd burst from his rectum, when you'd least
expect them
With the force of a raging typhoon

I once asked a lady named Pott
Why does sucking your tits make you hot
Well if you must be blunt, they signal my cunt
That it's going to get what you got

There once was a man from Peru
Who fell asleep while in his canoe
He dreamed about Venus, and played with
his penis
And awoke with a handful of goo

'Twas another man from nantucket
Who sailed the sea in a bucket
When he got over there, they asked for his fare
So he pulled out his cock and said "suck it"

„Taco" Songbook from 1995

Fuckin' Hell She's Ugly

Tune: All I Want is a Room Somewhere

All I want is a whore somewhere,
Great big labia, no pubic hair,
Open mouth with no teeth there,
Oh fuckin' hell, she's ugerly, ugerly.

Great big tits that hang so slack,
One is yellow and the other black,
Oh man, have you seen her crack?
Oh fuckin' hell, she's ugerly, ugerly.

She's got stretch marks on her guts,
Just like all the other sluts,
An abortion scar that opens and shuts,
Oh fuckin' hell, she's ugerly, ugerly.

Took her home to meet me mum,
Dad saw her and nearly cum,
"Son," he said, "have you seen her bum?"
Oh fuckin' hell, she's ugerly, ugerly.

She's hunch backed with a broken nose,
Got one club foot with an ingrown toe,
Her menstrual flow comes out of her nose,
Oh fuckin' hell, she's ugerly, ugerly.

She's got acne you wouldn't believe,
Broken teeth and breath like cheese,
Her pubic hair is alive with fleas,
Oh fuckin' hell, she's ugerly, ugerly.

She wears a wig 'cause she's got no hair,
The shit do cling to her underwear,
I should know 'cause I've been there,
Oh fuckin' hell, she's ugerly, ugerly.

Her wooden leg is far too short,
Her glass eye's got a list to port,
I've shagged her mum, she's such a sport,
Oh fuckin' hell, she's ugerly, ugerly.

I met her when she was thrity-five,

I looked into those criss-crossed eyes,
It was hard to tell if she was dead or alive,
Oh fuckin' hell, she's ugerly, ugerly.

She said, "Grab me by my private parts,"
As I did she blew out a fart,
Followed with a grunt from within her cunt,
Oh fuckin' hell, she's ugerly, ugerly.

Now she's dead and there ain't no more,
I fucked to death that rotten whore,
My balls are red and my dick's so sore,
Oh fuckin' hell, she's ugerly, ugerly.

Gang Bang

KNOCK KNOCK! *WHO'S THERE?*
ANITA. *ANITA WHO?*
I need a gang bang, I always will,
Because a gang bang gives me such a thrill.
When I was younger and in my prime,
I used to gang bang all the time.
But now I'm older and turning gray,
I only gang bang once a day.

...Ida...I'd a want another gang-bang...

...Eisenhower...I's an hour late for the gang bang?

...Wilma...Wilma finger do until I get a hard-on at the gang bang?

...Emma...Emma some nice tits, glad you brought 'em to the gang bang...

...Gladiator...Gladiator out before the gang bang...

...Banana...Bananananana, na na na na, ...

...Orange...Orange you glad I didn't say Bananananana, na na na na....

...Reagan...Reagan brought his own Bush to the gang bang...

...Ben Hur...Ben Hur over the couch, we need a gang bang...

...Nixon...Nixon the blow job, I need a gang bang...

...Tom Sawyer...Tom Sawyer mother at the gang bang...

...Ben...Ben dover and have another gang bang...

...Turner...Turner over and have another gang bang...

...Oliver...Oliver clothes were off at the gang bang...

...Peter Meter....My peter'll meet her at the gang bang...

...Kissinger...Kissinger's great but fuckin' her's better at the gang bang...

...Betty...Bet he'll have a sore dick after the gang bang...

...Sharon...Sharon share alike at the gang bang...

...Kenya...Kenya gimme directions to the gang bang...

General Guinness

You've heard of General Wellington
Who won at Waterloo,
But there's a good old Irishman
I'll introduce to you
He comes from dear old Dublin
He's a man we all applaud
For he always finds a corkscrew
Far more hardy than a sword.
He's good old General Guinness
He's a soldier strong and stout
Found on every battlefront
He can't be done without
His noble name has worldwide fame
Preserved through hearty cheers
Hurrah for General Guinness
And the Dublin Boozileers!

This hale and hearty warrior
Is worshipped in the ranks,
For he does his task inside a cask
As well as in the tanks.
He's borne the brunt on every front,
North, South, East and West,
And he wears about ten thousand canteen

Medals on his chest.
He's good old General Guinness.
He's won the world's applause.
It was he who kept our spirits up
In the midst of all the wars.
Who was the first to flirt with
Mademoiselle from Armentiers?
Why good old General Guinness
Of the Dublin Boozileers.

All over bonny Scotland, too,
The General is seen.
They've given him the freedom
Of the town of Aberdeen.
From Inverness to Galloshiles,
They keep him warm at night
And they love to gather round him,
Auuuch! On every moonlit night.
He's good old General Guinness
He's as good as Scottish broth.
He's the one who turned the Firth of Forth
Into the Firth of Froth
All Scotsmen dance the highland fling
And shout when he appears
Hurrah for General Guinness
And the Dublin Boozileers!

Geoff's Song

Tune: You've lost that loving feeling

You better watch your step ever more, in case your foot slips.
'Cos there's no tenderness, like before in that fingertip,
They tried so hard to resew it, Geoffrrey.
But, Geoffrey we know it-
You,ve lost that little finger,
Wo-oo that little finger.
You've lost that little finger,
Now it's gone, gone, gone, gone up there.
Da dum, da dum, da dum, dada da dum……..
But Geoffrey we know-
You just went to walk down the stairs,
And at the bottom your finger was still up there!

Geordie

As I walked out over London Bridge,
One misty morning early,
I overheard a fair pretty maid
Lamenting for her Geordie.

Ah my Geordie will be hanged in a golden chain,
It's not the chain of many.
He was born of king's royal breed,
And lost to a virtuous lady.

Go bridle me my milkwhite steed,
Go bridle me my pony,
And I will ride to London's court
To save the life of Geordie.

Ah my Geordie never stole no cow nor calf,
He never hurted any,
He stole sixteen of the King's royal deer
And sold them in Bohenny.

The judge looked over his left shoulder,
He said "Fair maid, I'm sorry",
He said "Fair maid, you must be gone,
For I cannot pardon Geordie".

Ah my Geordie will be hanged in a golden chain,
It's not the chain of many.
He stole sixteen of the King's royal deer
And sold them in Bohenny.

Gilliagan's Island

Tune: Gilligan's Island Theme

Just sit right back and you'll hear a tale,
A tale of a fateful trip,
That started with a drippy dick,
And a cold sore on my lip.

The skipper started getting rough,
He grabbed my scrotum sack,
Pulled it back between my legs,
And shoved it up my crack.

The professor sucked off Mary Anne,
And Thurston Howell the 3rd
Was nuzzlin' Gilligan's asshole,
Hopin' for a turd.

Mrs Howell and Ginger were doin' 69,
Ginger thought her period was late . . .
But it was right on time!

Glorious, Victorious (Beer, Beer, Beer)

Beer, beer, beer, beer, beer, beer, beer, beer
Drunk last night, drunk the night before,
Gonna get drunk tonight like I've never been drunk before,
Cause when I'm drunk I'm as happy as can be,
Cause we're all part of the Souse family.
Oh the Souse Family is the best family
To ever come over from Old Germany.
There's the Highland Dutch and the Lowland Dutch
the Rotterdam Dutch and the Goddam Dutch.
singing glorius, vic-torious!
One keg of beer for the four of us.
Singing Glory be to God that there are no more of us,
Cause one of us could drink it all alone
Damn near, pass the beer, to the rear, of the squadron!

Ghost Fuckers In The Sky

Tune: Ghost Riders In The Sky

An old cowpoke went riding out, one dark and windy day.
Stopped beneath a shady tree, and paused to beat his meat.
When all at once a slant eyed bitch, came ridin' down the trail.
He stopped her and asked her, "How 'bout a piece of tail?"

Chorus:

Yipee-yi-yeaaaa, Yipee-yi-yooooo
Ghost fuckers in the sky!

Her tits were a floppin', her cunt ate out with clap.
He socked it to her anyway, and gave her ass a slap.
She shit, she moaned, she groaned, she threw him from her crack,
He rolled across the desert and broke his fucking back.

Green Grow The Rushes O

Tune: Green Grow the Rushes O

Green grow the rashes O,
Green grow the rashes O,
The sweetest bed I ever had,
Was the bellies of the lassies O.

We're all full from eating it,
We're all dry from drinking it,
The parson kissed the fiddler's wife,
And couldn't preach for thinking of it.

There's a pious lass in town
Godly Lizzy Lundy O,
She mounts the peak throughout the week,
But fingers it on Sunday O.

Lizzie is of large dimension,
There is not a doubt of it,
The soccer team went in last night,
And none has yet come out of it.

Jockie's wife she thought she'd shave it,
Threw him in a pretty passion,
Shouting he'd not have a wife,
Whose private parts were out of fashion.

Hail Britannia

Hail Britannia, marmalade and jam,
Three Chinese crackers up you asshole
BAM BAM BAM

Hail Britannia, marmalade and jam,
Two Chinese crackers up you asshole
BAM BAM

Hail Britannia, marmalade and jam,
One Chinese cracker up you asshole
BAM

A Lightning Flash Production:

Unofficial Fighter Pilots Songbook

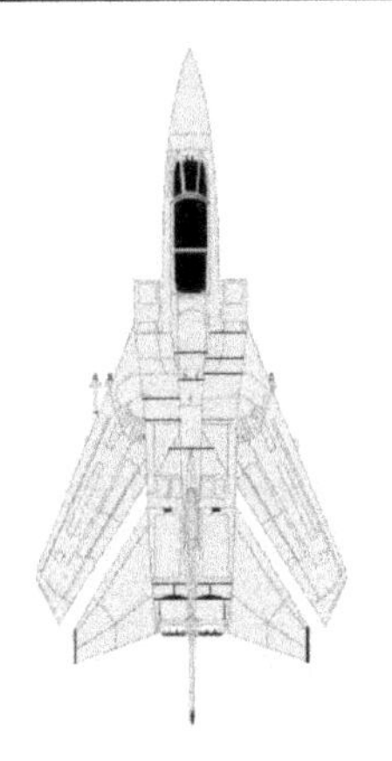

A compilation of songs, poems and quotes from
Messes, Officers Clubs and Crewrooms.

From a RAF SQN.

He Ought To Be Publicly Pissed On

Tune: My Bonnie Lies Over the Ocean

He ought to be publicly pissed on,
He ought to be publicly shot,
He ought to be tied to a urinal,
And left there to fester and rot.
He ought to be hung, drawn, and quartered,
He ought to be dragged through the street,
He ought to be publicly horsewhipped,
And flogged on the soles of his feet.
Piss on, piss on, piss on this pile of shit, of shit!
Piss on, piss on, piss on this pile of shit!

Heigh-Ho Says Rowley

Tune: Froggie Goes A'Courtin'

A is for asshole all covered in shit,
Heigh-ho says Rowley,
B is the bugger who revels in it,
Singing roly, poly, up'em and stuff'em,
Heigh-ho, says Anthony Rowley.

C is for cunt all dripping with piss,
Heigh-ho, etc . . .
D is the drunkard who gave it a kiss, etc . . .

E is the eunuch with only one ball,
F is the fucker with no balls at all.

G is for goiter, gonorrhea, and gout,
H is the harlot who spreads it about.

I for insertion, injection, and itch,
J is the jerk of a dog on a bitch.

K is the knight who thought fucking a bore,
L is the lesbian who came back for more.

M is the maidenhead, tattered and torn,
N is the noble who died on his horn.

O is for orifice, cunningly concealed,
P is for penis, pranged up and peeled.

Q is the Quaker who shat in his hat,
R is the Rajah who rogered the cat.

S is the shit-pot, filled to the brim,
T are the turds which are floating within.

U is the usher who taught us at school,
V is the virgin who played with his tool.

W is the whore who thought fucking a farce,
And X, Y, and Z you can shove up your arse!

Hello Penis

Tune: Sound of Silence

Hello penis my old friend,
I've come to play with you again,
When those wet dreams come a-creeping,
I spurt my seeds while I am sleeping,
And with your helmet firmly planted in my hand,
It will expand,
While jerking off in silence.

In horny dreams I get a bone,
I beat me off on cobble stones,
Beneath the halo of a street lamp,
I see a whore who's getting very damp,
And for fifty gonks in a flash she's on her back,
She spreads her crack,
And twitches her twat in silence.

For those who see and do not know
How to make my penis grow,
I whipped you out so that she might eat you,
I stuffed you up into her pussy spew,
And then my sperm, like silent raindrops fell,
And turned to gel,
While jerking off in silence.

And the ants came out and played,
In the fucking mess I'd made,
But I rememberd still my dad's warning,
That mum would find it still in the morning,
So I rolled out of bed and wiped it up with my shirt,

God, what a squirt!
Jerking off in silence.

Here's To Brother ________

Tune: Ach, Du Lieber, Augustin

Here's to Brother __________, Brother __________, Brother __________,
Here's to Brother __________, he's uglier than shit.
He eats it, he beats it, he even mistreats it,
Here's to Brother __________, he's uglier than shit.
He's happy, he's jolly, he's fucked up by golly,
Here's to Brother __________, he's uglier than shit.
So DRINK motherfucker, DRINK motherfucker, DRINK motherfucker, DRINK...

Here's to Brother __________, he's uglier than shit!

Home For A Rest

Chorus:

> *You'll have to excuse me, I'm not at my best*
> *I've been gone for a month, I've been drunk since I left*
> *These so-called vacations will soon be my death*
> *I'm so sick from the drink, I need home for a rest...*

We arrived in December and London was cold
So we stayed in the bars along Charing Cross Road
We never saw nothin' but brass taps and oak
Kept a shine on the bar with the sleeves of our coats

Euston Station the train journey north
In the buffet car we lurched back and forth
Past odd crooked dikes, through Yorkshire's green fields
We were flung into dance as the train jigged and reeled

By the light of the moon she'd drift through the streets
A rare old perfume so seductive and sweet
She'd tease us and flirt as the pubs all closed down
Then walk us on home and deny us a round

The gas heater's empty, it's damp as a tomb
And the spirits we drank are now ghosts in the room

I'm knackered again, come on sleep take me soon
And don't lift up my head 'til the twelve bells of noon.

How About A 69

Tune: When I'm 64

I could be happy, licking your clit
When your pants are down.
You could suck my penis by the fireside,
Hop on board, let's go for a ride.
Out in the garden, top of the fridge,
Anywhere is fine.
Got an erection,
Got no protection,
So how about a 69?

When I get older, losing my balls
From my leprosy,
Will you still be sucking on the rotten bits,
Rubbing pus all over your tits?
Woke up this morning,
To my surprise,
My cock I could not find.
Just gotta face it,
Must've misplaced it,
So how about a 69?

Send you a parcel
Enclosing my balls, and my foreskin too.
Telling you the thing I find it hard to say,
Yours sincerely, wasting away.
Just can't seem to
Get any joy
From this stump of mine.
I can't ignore it,
Nothing else for it,
So, how about a 69?

How The Money Rolls In

Tune: My Bonnie Lies Over the Ocean

My father makes book on the corner,
My mother makes synthetic gin;
My sister sells blowjobs to sailors,
My God, how the money rolls in.

Chorus:

Rolls in, rolls in
My God, how the money rolls in, rolls in.
Rolls in, rolls in
My God, how the money rolls in.

My mother's a bawdy house keeper,
Each night when the evening grows dim,
She hangs out a little red lantern,
My God how the money rolls in.

My cousin's a Harley Street surgeon,
With instruments long, short and thin.
He only does one operation,
My God, how the money rolls in.

My brother's a slum missionary,
He saves fallen women from sin.
He'll save you a blonde for a five dollars.
My God, how the money rolls in.

My aunt keeps a girl's seminary,
Teaching young girls to begin.
She won't tell me where they will finish,
My God how the money rolls in.

My sister's a barmaid in Sydney,
For a shilling she'll strip to the skin,
She's stripping from morning till midnight,
My God how the money rolls in.

My grandmother rolls prophylactics,
My grandpa pokes them with a pin,
My uncle performs the abortions,
My God, how the money rolls in.

My one skin lies over my two skin,
My two skin lies over my three.
My three skin lies over my four skin,
So pull back my foreskin for me.

Pull back, pull back,
Oh, pull back my foreskin for me, for me.
Pull back, Pull back,
Oh, pull back my foreskin for me.

I Fucked A Dead Whore By Te Roadside

Tune: My Bonnie Lies Over the Ocean

I fucked a dead whore by the roadside
I knew right away she was dead
The skin was all gone from her tummy
The hair was all gone from her head
As I laid down there beside her
I knew right away I had sinned
So I pressed my lips to her sweet pussy
And sucked out the wad I shot in

Sucked out, sucked out
I sucked out the wad I'd shot in
Sucked out, sucked out
I sucked out the wad I'd shot in

My one skin lies over my two skin
My two skin lies over my three
My three skin lies over my foreskin
Oh, bring back my foreskin to me

Bring back, bring back
Oh, bring back my foreskin to me
Bring back, bring back
Oh, bring back my foreskin to me

Patty cake, patty cake, baker man
If your chicks on her period,
FUCK HER IN THE CAN!!!

Hey diddle, diddle, the cat and the fiddle,
The cow jumped over the moon.
That's more than my wife does,
THAT FAT, FUCKING SMELLY BABOON!!!

Little Bo Peep, fucked all her sheep,
Blew, a horse, licked his feet,
She ate his ass so very nice,
TOUNGUED HIS BALLS NOT ONCE, BUT TWICE!!!

Eenie meenie miney moe,
SUCK MY DICK AND SWALLOW SLOW!!!
Twinkle twinkle little star
How I wonder where you are,

Shine upon my parking lot,
AS I EAT MY GIRLFRIENDS TWAT!!!

Little Jack Horner sat in the corner, eating a pizza pie,
He blew his friend Tony, shit pepperoni,
AND WIPED HIS MOUTH WITH HIS TIE!!!
There was a young man from Sparta
Who was the world's champion farter
On the strength of one bean
He played "God Save the Queen"
And Beethoven's Moonlight Sonata.

There was a young man from Dundee
Who buggered an ape in a tree
The result was most horrid, all ass and no forehead
Three balls and a purple goatee.

There once was a man of class
Whose balls were made out of brass
When they swung together, they played stormy weather
And lightening shot out of his ass.

There once was a man from Rangoon
Who was born nine months to soon
He didn't have the luck to be born by a fuck
He was scraped off the sheets with a spoon.

There once was girl named Flo Varden
Who went down on a guy in the garden
He said "Listen Flo, where does all that stuff go?"
And she said, "[GULP] Beg pardon?"

There once was a man from Wheeling
Who pounded his pud with great feeling
And just like a trout, he'd stick his mouth out
And wait for the drops from the ceiling.

There once was a man from Brighton
Who said, "My dear you've a tight one"
She said, "Oh, my soul, you've got the wrong hole,
It's the one up front that's the right one."

There once was a boy from Baclaridge,
And was his parents disparage
He sucked off his brother, and went down on his mother,
And ate up his sister's miscarriage

There once was a pilot from K-2,
Who buggered a girl in Taegu.
He said to the Doc, as he handed him his cock,
Will I lose both my testicles, too?
In the Garden of Eden sat Adam,
With his hand on the butt of his madam.
He chuckled with mirth, for he knew on this earth,
There were only two balls and he had them.

There once was a man from Trieste,
Who loved his wife with zest.
Despite all her howls, he sucked out her bowels,
And deposited the mess on her breasts.

There once was a man from Kildare,
Who buggered his girl on the stairs.
The banister broke, so he doubled the stroke,
And finished her off in midair.

There once was a man from St. James,
Who played most unusual games.
He lit a match to his grandmother's snatch,
And laughed as he pissed through the flames,

There once was a young Bishop from Birmingham,
Who diddled nuns while confirming 'em.
He brought them indoors, and slipped down their drawers,
And slipped his Episcopal worm in 'em.

I Have A Dog His Name Is Fritz

I have a dog his name is Rover.
OH MY GOODNESS!
I have a dog his name is Rover.
EEE BY GUM!
I have a dog his name is Rover,
And when he shits he shits all over.
SHIT ALL ROUND THE ROOM ME BOYS,
SHIT ALL ROUND THE ROOM.

I have a dog his name is Fritz.
OH MY GOODNESS!
I have a sausage dog his name is Fritz.
EEE BY GUM!

I have a dog his name is Fritz,
And when he shits, he shits and shits,
SHIT ALL ROUND THE ROOM ME BOYS,
SHIT ALL ROUND THE ROOM.

I have a dog a big Great Dane.
OH MY GOODNESS!
I have a dog a big Great Dane.
EEE BY GUM!
I've got a dog a big Great Dane,
He wipes his bum and pulls the chain.
SHIT ALL ROUND THE ROOM ME BOYS,
SHIT ALL ROUND THE ROOM.

7440th COMBAT SONG BOOK

Dedicated in the spirit of all fighter jocks, living and dead, especially those who have been shot at.

CONTENTS

"If you have to have a real job, this isn't a bad one to have."
-Jimmy Buffett

7440TH COMBAT
SONG BOOK
INCIRLIK AB, TURKEY

17 JAN - 28 FEB 1991

23TFS, 38TRS, 525TFS, 32TFG, 612TFS, 79TFS, 55TFS, 42ECS, 43ECS, 192SOG, 804ARW, 7SOS, 21SOS, 67SOS, 552AWACW

I Love My Wife

Chorus:

I love my wife, yes I do, yes I do,
I love her truly.
I love the hole that she pisses through.

I love her ruby red lips, her lily white tits,
And the hair around her asshole.

I'd eat her shit,
Gobble, gobble, slurp, slurp,
With a rusty spoon, with a rusty spoon.

Chorus:

I love her matted black hair, and her dirty underwear
And the smell of her vagina
I'd eat her cunt
gobble, gobble, slurp, slurp,
If she asked me to, if she asked me to.

„A Night at the Bar with the Boys ..... a Fighter Pilot songfest"
The CD was recorded in St. Thomas Church, Glenhooha, Scotland in 1989.

This CD was for sure a landmark, to "throttle back", and stop to continue moving the moral borders.

I Need A Ewe

Tune: Scotland the Brave

Bring me some whiskey, mother,
I'm feeling frisky, mother.
I need a ewe to keep me warm through the night!
I need a lover, mother,
No, not my brother, mother.
I need a ewe to keep me warm through the night!

Gerbils don't make it, mother,
They just can't take it, mother.
I need a ewe to keep me warm through the night!
Owls, bats and other critters,
Just tend to give me jitters.
I need a ewe to keep me warm through the night!

Ewes never talk about it,
They never ever doubt it.
Always so placid, affectionate and nice!
Give me that lanolin,
Better than flannel-in.
I need a ewe to keep me warm through the night!

I Put My Hand

Tune: When Johnny Comes Marching Home

Now gather around and I'll tell you a tale, Ya Ho! Ya Ho!
Now gather around and I'll tell you a tale, Ya Ho! Ya Ho!
Now gather around and I'll tell you a tale,
About a girl we did from Yale,
Get in, get out, quit fuckin' about!
Ya Ho! Ya Ho! Ya Ho!

I put my hand upon her toe, Ya Ho! Ya Ho!
I put my hand upon her toe, Ya Ho! Ya Ho!
I put my hand upon her toe,
She said, "Hey ________________, you're way too low,
Get in, get out, quit fuckin' about!"
Ya Ho! Ya Ho! Ya Ho!

I put my hand upon her shin, Ya Ho! Ya Ho!
I put my hand upon her shin, Ya Ho! Ya Ho!
I put my hand upon her shin,

She said, "Hey ________________, you're makin' me grin,
Get in, get out, quit fuckin' about!"
Ya Ho! Ya Ho! Ya Ho!

I put my hand upon her calf, Ya Ho! Ya Ho!
I put my hand upon her calf, Ya Ho! Ya Ho!
I put my hand upon her calf,
She said, "Hey ________________, you're makin' me laugh,
Get in, get out, quit fuckin' about!"
Ya Ho! Ya Ho! Ya Ho!

I put my hand upon her knee, Ya Ho! Ya Ho!
I put my hand upon her knee, Ya Ho! Ya Ho!
I put my hand upon her knee,
She said, "Hey ________________, you're teasin' me,
Get in, get out, quit fuckin' about!"
Ya Ho! Ya Ho! Ya Ho!

I put my hand upon her thigh, Ya Ho! Ya Ho!
I put my hand upon her thigh, Ya Ho! Ya Ho!
I put my hand upon her thigh,
She said, "Hey ________________, you're makin' me high,
Get in, get out, quit fuckin' about!"
Ya Ho! Ya Ho! Ya Ho!

I put my hand upon her tit, Ya Ho! Ya Ho!
I put my hand upon her tit, Ya Ho! Ya Ho!
I put my hand upon her tit,
She said, "Hey ________________, you're squeezin' it,
Get in, get out, quit fuckin' about!"
Ya Ho! Ya Ho! Ya Ho!

I put my hand upon her twat, Ya Ho! Ya Ho!
I put my hand upon her twat, Ya Ho! Ya Ho!
I put my hand upon her twat,
She said, "Hey ________________, you've hit the spot,
Get in, get out, quit fuckin' about!"
Ya Ho! Ya Ho! Ya Ho!

I put my hand upon her clit, Ya Ho! Ya Ho!
I put my hand upon her clit, Ya Ho! Ya Ho!
I put my hand upon her clit,
She said, "Hey ________________, you've finally found it!
Get in, get out, quit fuckin' about!"
Ya Ho! Ya Ho! Ya Ho!

I put my cock into her eye, Ya Ho! Ya Ho!
I put my cock into her eye, Ya Ho! Ya Ho!
I put my cock into her eye,
She said, "Hey ________________, you're way too high!
Get in, get out, quit fuckin' about!"
Ya Ho! Ya Ho! Ya Ho!

I put my cock into her ear, Ya Ho! Ya Ho!
I put my cock into her ear, Ya Ho! Ya Ho!
I put my cock into her ear,
She said, "Hey ________________, you're nowhere near!
Get in, get out, quit fuckin' about!"
Ya Ho! Ya Ho! Ya Ho!

I put my cock upon her chin, Ya Ho! Ya Ho!
I put my cock upon her chin, Ya Ho! Ya Ho!
I put my cock upon her chin,
She said, "Hey ________________, please stick it in!
Get in, get out, quit fuckin' about!"
Ya Ho! Ya Ho! Ya Ho!

I put my cock into her mouth, Ya Ho! Ya Ho!
I put my cock into her mouth, Ya Ho! Ya Ho!
I put my cock into her mouth,
She said, "AAAAAUGH, MMMMMPH, THHHPT!
Get in, get out, quit fuckin' about!"
Ya Ho! Ya Ho! Ya Ho!

Now she lies in a wooden box, Ya Ho! Ya Ho!
Now she lies in a wooden box, Ya Ho! Ya Ho!
Now she lies in a wooden box,
From sucking too many ________________'s cocks,
Get in, get out, quit fuckin' about!
Ya Ho! Ya Ho! Ya Ho!

We dig her up every now and again, Ya Ho! Ya Ho!
We dig her up every now and again, Ya Ho! Ya Ho!
We dig her up every now and again,
She did us before, and she'll do us again!
Get in, get out, quit fuckin' about!
Ya Ho! Ya Ho! Ya Ho!

I Want to Play Piano In A Whorehouse

I want to play piano in a whorehouse
That is but my one desire
Some may want to be rancers or farmers out in Butte,
I just want to play in this house of ill repute
Don't deny me my humble aspiration,
For carnal copulation's here to stay
I don't want no fame or riches,
I just want to play for those old bitches
I want to play piano in a whorehouse.

If I Where The Marrying Kind

Chorus:

> *If I were the marrying kind,*
> *Which thank the Lord I'm not, sir,*
> *The kind of man that I would be*
> *Would be a rugby…*

Prop, Sir.
...A Prop, Sir?
I'd support hookers, you'd support hookers
We'd all support hookers together.
We'd be all right in the middle of the night,
Supporting hookers together.

Chorus:

> *Would be a rugby…*

Scrum Half, Sir.
...A Scrum Half, Sir?
Oh, I'd put it in, you'd put it in,
We'd both put it in together.
We'd be all right in the middle of the night,
Putting it in together.

Prop: I'd bind tight, she'd bind tight, we'd both bind tight together...
Hooker: I'd hook balls...
Lock: I'd sniff butt…
8-Man: I'd split cheeks…
Flanker: I'd hold it in
Fly-half: I'd whip it out
Stand-off: I'd pass it on

Winger: I'd get none
Groundskeeper: I'd trim bush
Goal Post: I'd stand erect
Referee's Whistle: I'd get blown
Water Bottle: I'd get sucked
Rugby Boot: I'd get smelly
Cleat: I'd get screwed
Ball: I'd get pumped
Center: I'd put it out, she'd put it out, we'd both put out together...
Fullback: I'd find touch, she'd find touch, we both would touch each other…
Referee #1: I'd fuck her, she'd fuck me, we both would fuck together...
Referee #2: I'd blow her, she'd blow me, we both would blow each other...
Spectator in the rain #1: I'd get wet
Spectator in the rain #2: I'd come in rubbers
Fair Weather Spectator: I'd come again

I'll Never Piss Again

Tune: Battle Hymn of the Republic

My dick has felt the burning of the coming of the clap,
I've been clean all these years and now I've got a real bum rap,
That bitch said she was clean, but surely she's a goddamn liar,
'Cause now my dick's on fire.

Chorus:

Lordy, Lordy I'm on fire, Lordy, Lordy I'm on fire,
Lordy, Lordy I'm on fire, and I'll never piss again.

I saw her coming at me from across a burlesque bar,
Her ass was swinging wildly and her tits were sagging far,
I propped her on a barstool and I bought that bitch a drink,
Then I smelled that telltale stink.

Swedish Bees, Kamikazes, Stolies, and some brew,
My dick was getting hard, man, the big old Wally grew,
She reached into my pants and she pulled that monster out,
And I began to scream and shout...

Well I should have listened to him 'cause he'd been with her before,
That must have been where he got that bloody festered sore,
I should have listened to him when he said she was a whore,
But you know "Bo needs more."

Now I'm in the doctor's office sitting in the chair,
Nothing like a red hot poker way down deep in there,
The doctor pushed too far and my scrotum began to tear,
Oh God, this really SUCKS.

I'm A Darlin'

Tune: "Dublin City"

As I walked out of Chester city
At the late hour of the night
Who should I see but a fair young maiden
Washing her clothes by the clear moonlight

Chorus: Madam, I'm a darlin', a die-ro-dither-o
Madam, I'm a darlin', a die-ro-day

First she washed and then she squeezed them
And then she hung them out to dry
And then she folded up her arms saying
O what a fair young girl am I

O, going to the well to fetch some water
Fetching it back to make some cheese
She fell under and I fell over
And all the game was above her knee

Madam I will tie your garter,
I will tie it above your knee
And if you like I'll tie it up farther
'Cause madam I'm a die-row-day

Have you ever heard of cups and saucers
Rattling round an old tin can
have you ever heard of a fair young girl
Married to an ugly grey old man

Madam you may have the gold and silver
Madam you may have the tracts of land
You may have ships all on the ocean
But what you need now is a canny young man.

Im München Steht in Hofbräuhaus

Da, wo die grüne Isar fließt,
Wo man mit "Grüß Gott" dich grüßt,
Liegt meine schöne Münch'ner Stadt,
Die ihresgleichen nicht hat.
Wasser ist billig, rein und gut,
Nur verdünnt es unser Blut,
Schöner sind Tropfen gold'nen Wein's,
Aber am schönsten ist eins:

In München steht ein Hofbräuhaus:
Eins, zwei, g'suffa . . .
Da läuft so manches Fäßchen aus:
Eins, zwei, g'suffa . . .
Da hat so manche braver Mann:
Eins, zwei, g'suffa . . .
Gezeigt was er so vertragen kann
Schon früh am Morgen fing er an
Und spät am Abend kam er heraus
So schön ist's im Hofbräuhaus.

Da trinkt man Bier nicht aus dem Glas,
Da gibt's nur "die große Maß!"
Und wenn der erste Maßkrug leer,
Bringt dir die Reserl bald mehr.
Oft kriegt zu Haus die Frau 'nen Schreck,
Bleibt der Mann mal länger weg.
Aber die braven Nachbarsleut',
Die wissen besser Bescheid!

In München steht ein Hofbräuhaus: . . . . .

Wenn auch so manche schöne Stadt
Sehenswürdigkeiten hat,
Eins gibt es nirgendwo wie hier:
Das ist das Münchener Bier.
Wer dieses kleine Lied erdacht
Hat so manche lange Nacht
Über dem Münchener Bier studiert
Und hat es gründlich probiert.

Ivan Skavinsky Scavar

The harems of Egypt are fine to behold,
The harlots the fairest of fair,
But the fairest of all was owned by a sheik, named Abdul Abulbul Emir.

A traveling brothel came down from the north,
'Twas privately run for the Czar,
Who wagered a hundred no one could outshag, Ivan Skavinsky Scavar.

A day was arranged for the spectacle great,
A holiday proclaimed by the Czar,
And the streets were all lined with the harlots assigned, to Ivan Skavinsky Scavar.

All hairs they were shorn, no frenchies were worn,
And this suited Abdul by far,
And he quite set his mind on a fast action grind, to beat Ivan Skavinsky Scavar.

They met on the track with cocks at the slack,
A starter's gun punctured the air,
They were both quick to rise, the crowd gaped at the size, of Abdul Abulbul Emir.

They worked all the night in the pale yellow light,
Old Abdul he revved like a car,
But he couldn't compete with the slow steady beat, of Ivan Skavinsky Scavar.

So Ivan he won and he shouldered his gun,
He bent down to polish the pair,
When something red hot up his back passage shot, 'twas Abdul Abulbul Emir.

The harlots turned green, the crowd shouted "Queen,"
They were ordered apart by the Czar,
'Twas bloody bad luck for poor Abdul was stuck, up Ivan Skavinsky Scavar.

The cream of the joke came when they broke,
'Twas laughed at for years by the Czar,
For Abdul, the fool, left half of his tool, up Ivan Skavinsky Scavar.

I've Got A Start On A Twelve Inch Hard-On

Tune: I'm Looking Over a Four Leaf Clover

I've got a start on a twelve-inch hard-on
That I've had all afternoon.
Went to the doctor, he told me to cough,
I wish that he would have whacked it right off!
Come to me, Venus, massage my penis,
And shrivel it like a prune,
'Cause I've got a start on a twelve-inch hard-on
I'll probably have till June, till June.
I'll probably have till June.

Jocelyn Elders

Tune: Yankee Doodle
(Composed by Flying Booger)

Jocelyn Elders lay in bed,
A-rubbin' on her plumbing,
She thought it safer than a lay,
The only way for cumming.

Jocelyn Elders, stir it up,
Jocylyn, are you randy?
Jocelyn Elders, rub it hard,
You are so very handy.

Jug O' Punch

As I was walking one fine morning
In the month of June, by the jug and spoon,
A birdie sat on an ivy bunch,
And the song it sang was a jug o' punch.

Chorus:

> *Too-ra-loo-ra-loo, too-ra-loo-ra-loo*
> *Too-ra-loo-ra-loo, too-ra-loo-ra-loo*
> *A birdie sat on an ivy bunch,*
> *And the song it sang was a jug o' punch.*

What more perversion can a man desire
Than to whip his girl by an open fire,
A kerry pipin to crackle and crunch,

Aye and on the table a jug o' punch

Even the doctor with all his art,
Cannot cure a man of a broken heart,
Even the cripple forgets his hunch,
When he's safe outside of a jug o' punch.

When I am dead and I am in my grave,
There is just on thing, that I do crave,
Just lay me down in my native peat,
With a jug o' punch at my head and feet.

Kotex Song

You can tell by her smell that she isn't feeling well,
When the end of the month rolls around.
You can tell by her dance she has something in her pants,
When the end of the month CUMS around.

Chorus:

For it's HI, HI, HEE in the KOTEX factory,
Shout out your orders loud and clear
We got SUPER, REGULAR, LARGE
We got RAGS to fit a bargeWhen the end of the month rolls around.

You know she'll be horny when she's on the cotton pony,
You can feel from her lovin' that she's leaking hemoglobin,

If you're looking like the JOKER, then you'd better not POKER,
If she's acting pretty sad, you know she's on the pad,

You'd better give it up the rump, or you'll have a bloody stump,
You can tell from the taste, that it's not Salmon paste,

You can tell from the string, that there's something up her thing,
You can tell by the bed, that her little pussy bled,

You can tell from the sight, that the taste will have a bite,
You can tell by the feel, that she's stating to congeal,

She'll be really dry and tight, by the end of the night,
She'll bleed on your rug, if you pull out your plug,

If she has a yeast infection, better clean your erection,

You can tell that she's sick form the color of your prick,

You can tell by the stress, that she's having PMS,
If her pussy's flowin' red, just get some head,

You'll see lots of blood, when you pull out your pud,
If the smell's really heinous, you'll have to use her anus,

How she turns, how she squirms, how she gets a case of worms,
Your can tell from the strain, that you hit a major vein.

Lady Hardonna

Melody - Lady Madonna

Lady Hardonna, men at your feet,
Wonder how you manage to beat their meat.
You find the money, when you need to pay the rent,
You know that money isn't heaven sent.
Friday's guy arrives without a suitcase,
Sunday's Hasher creeps in like a bum,
Monday's guy likes to be tied with his boot lace,
See how they'll come.

Lady Hardonna, Hasher at your breast,
Wonder how you manage to please the rest?
Lady Hardonna, lying on the bed,
No worry about losing your maidenhead.
Tuesday's love is never ending,
Wednesday morning milkman didn't come,
Thursday night your diaphragm needed mending,
See how they'll come.

Lady Hardonna, Hashers at your feet,
Wonder how you manage to beat their meat?

Let's Have A Party

Tune: Money Makes the World Go Around

Chorus:

Parties make the world go around,
The world go around, the world go around,
Parties make the world go around,
Let's have a party!

We're gonna tear down the bar!	BOO!
We're gonna build a new bar!	RAY!
One inch deep!	BOO!
Two miles long!	RAY!
Soda's goinna be five dollars a glass!	BOO!
Whiskey's gonna be free!	RAY!
We're gonna dump the beer in the pool!	BOO!
Then we're all going swimming!	RAY!
There'll be no bartenders at our bar!	BOO!
Only barmaids!	RAY!
In long dresses!	BOO!
Made of cellophane!	RAY!
You can't take our girls to your rooms!	BOO!
Our girls'll take you to their rooms!	RAY!
But you can't sleep with our girls!	BOO!
Our girls won't let you sleep!	RAY!
No fuckin' on the dancin' floor!	BOO!
And no dancin' on the fuckin' floor!	RAY!

Let Me Call You Sweethart

Let me call you sweetheart, I'm in love with you.
Let me stroke your vulva, 'till it fills with goo.
Let me bite your boobies, 'till their black and blue.
Let's play hide the weenie, up the old wazoo.

Leprosy

Tune: Yesterday

Leprosy, all my skin is falling off of me,
I'm not half the man I used to be,
Oh, why did I get leprosy?...

Syphilis, it only started with a simple kiss,
Now it even hurts to take a piss,
Oh, why did I get Syphilis?...

Why her BOX is sick, I don't know, she wouldn't say...
Now my DRIPPING DICK won't get thick like
Yes—ter—dayayayayayayayay.........

Yesterday, my dick was always coming out to play,

Now it needs two weeks to hide away,
Oh, I believe in yes—ter—day....
MMMM, MMMM, MMMM, MMMM, MMMM....

Lily White Kidney Wiper

Chorus:

(Repeat after each verse)
With that Lily White Kidney Wiper
And balls the size of these
And a half a yard foreskin
A hangin' down below the knees.
Hangin' down (WHAT A PRICK)
Hangin' down (INCHES THICK)
And a half a yard foreskin
A hangin' down below his knees,

Oh, the lady of the manor
Was dressing for the ball (3)
When she heard the Highland Tinker
A humping 'ginst the wall. (3)

So, she wrote to him a letter
And in it she did say (3)
I'd rather be fucked by you, sir
Than my husband any day. (3)

Lupe

Tune - Sweet Betsy From Pike

'Twas down in cunt valley where red rivers flow,
Where cocksuckers flourish and maidenheads grow,
'Twas there I met Lupe, the girl I adore,
She's a hot fucking, cocksucking, Mexican whore.

Chorus:

She'll fuck you, she'll suck you, she'll tickle your nuts,
And if you're not happy, she'll suck out your guts,
She'll wrap her legs round you till you want to die,
But I'd rather eat Lupe than sweet cherry pie.

When Lupe was a young girl of just about eight,
She'd swing to and fro on the back garden gate,

The crossmember parted, the upright went in,
And since then she's lived in a welter of sin.

Now Lupe is dead and she lays in her tomb,
The worms crawl around in her decomposed womb,
The smile on her face, well, it says "Give me more,
I'm a hot fucking, cocksucking, Mexican whore."

Loaded Too

Tune: Close to You

Why do geeks suddenly appears,
Every time I buy beer...
Just like me, they long to be,
LOADED TOO!!!
LAAAAAH, LAAEEEEEEAAAAEEEE, LOADED TOO!!!

On the day I got paid, my buddies got together,
And decide to try and scam some brew,
So they bellied right up to the bar,
And waited for me to buy some brew,
(badabump, badabump).

That is why all the geeks in town (geeks in town)
Follow me (follow me),
All around (all around)
Just like me, they long to be,
LOADED TOO!!!
LAAAAAH, LAAEEEEEEAAAAEEEE, LOADED TOO!!!

Madeline Schmidt

Tune: Sweet Betsy From Pike

(This song is also known as "Adelaine Schmidt." The second version, adapted for hashing, is from a Thailand hash songbook, authors unknown)

There was a young maiden named Madeline Schmidt,
Who went to the doctor 'cause she couldn't shit,
He gave her some medicine all wrapped up in glass,
Up went the window and out went her ass!
Chorus:
It was brown, brown, shit all around,

It was brown, brown, shit all around,
It was brown, brown, shit all around,
And the whole world was covered in SHIT, SHIT, SHIT, SHIT!

A handsome young copper was walking his beat,
He just happened to be on that side of the street,
He looked up so innocent, he looked up so shy,
And a big wad of shit hit him right in HIS EYE!

He turned to the east and he turned to the west,
Then a bloody great turd hit him right on the chest,
He turned to the north, then he turned to the south,
And another great turd hit him right in HIS MOUTH!

That handsome young copper he cursed and he swore,
He called that young maiden a dirty old whore,
And beneath London Bridge you can still see him sit,
With a sign 'round his neck saying BLINDED BY SHIT!

Two fast moving Hashers came running along,
Throwing flour and paper and singing their song,
Singing, Hi-Diddle-Diddle, and flogging their dongs,
The hares were trail-setting, the pack wouldn't be long.

The hares found the copper alone by the pit,
Threw flour in the holes where his eyes used to fit,
The hares led the pack by a block and a bit,
Said, "We'll lead the damn pack through these puddles of SHIT!"

The hares led the pack to the edge of the pit,
They slipped and they slid in the puddles of shit,
They fell in the shiggy, right up to their tails,
Ere they sank out of sight, they marked it TRUE TRAIL!

The pack followed bravely, the pack followed true,
They followed the hares into that vile brew,
They followed true trail right into the pit,
Soon the whole pack of Hashers was drowning in SHIT!

This tale has a lesson if you think a bit,
Don't follow true trail right into the pit,
Remember that hares can be damn bloody fools,
And in Hashing, like loving, there's NO FUCKING RULES!

Maggie May

Tune: ???

Oh, gather round you sailor boys,
And listen to my plea,
'Cause when you've heard it you will pity me.
'Cause I was a Goddamn fool,
In the port of Liverpool,
The first time that I came home from the sea.

Chorus:

Oh, my darling Maggie May,
They have taken her away,
And no more down Lime Street will she roam.
For the judge he guilty found her,
For robbing a homeward bounder,
That dirty, robbin', no good Maggie May.

I was a sailor bound for home,
All the way from Sierra Leone,
And two pound ten a month had been my pay.
As I jingled in my tin,
I was sadly taken in,
By the lady of the name of Maggie May.

When I steered into her,
I just hadn't a care,
I was cruisin' up and down ol' Canning Place.
She was dressed in a gown so fine,
Like a frigate of the line,
And I bein' a sailorman, I gave chase.

She gave me a saucy nod,
And I like a farmer's clod,
Let her take me line abreast in tow.
And under all plain sail,
We ran before the gale,
And to the Crow's Nest Tavern we did go.

Next morning when I awoke,
I found that I was broke,
No trousers, coat, or wallet could I find.
And when I asked her where,
She said, "My dear young sir,
You'll find them in the pawnshop, number nine."

To the pawnshop I did go,
No trousers could I find,
So the cops they came and took this girl away.
Oh, you thieving Maggie May,
You robbed me of my pay,
It'll pay your fare right out to Botany Bay.

She was chained and sent away,
From Liverpool one day,
The lads they cheered as she sailed down the bay.
And every sailor lad,
He only was too glad,
They'd sent the old tart out to Botany Bay.

Oh, Maggie, Maggie May,
They have taken you away,
For to stay on Van Dieman's cruel shore.
Oh, you robbed many a whaler,
And many a drunken sailor,
But you'll never cruise 'round Liverpool no more.

Magic Moments

Chorus:

Magic moments when two hearts are sharing
Magic moments filled with love

I'll never forget the smell of the sweat from her armpits
The smell of her crotch as much too much I just couldn't stand it

Chorus:

We went to a park just for a lark I pissed on the flowers
We sat on a bench I fingered the wench for hours and hours

Chorus:

Remember the night I got in a fight with my best suit on
The one that I got from saving a lot of embassy coupons
Chorus:

Remember the day we lay in they bay without any clothes on
You picked up a stick and battered my dick and now I ain't got one

Chorus:

Remember the night I fell in the shite with my best suit on
The one that I got from saving a lot of embassy coupons

Chorus:

Remember the day we had it away I gave you a shilling
The dose that you got required a lot of the doc's penicillin

Mary

Tune: London Bridge is Falling Down?

Mary in the kitchen punching duff, punching duff, punching duff,
Mary in the kitchen punching duff,
BULLSHIT!
Mary in the kitchen punching duff,
When the cheeks of her arse went chuff, chuff, chuff,
Shit all around the room, tra-la,
Shit all around the room.

Mary in the kitchen boiling rice, boiling rice, boiling rice,
Mary in the kitchen boiling rice,
BULLSHIT!
Mary in the kitchen boiling rice,
When out of her cunt jumped three blind mice,
Shit all around the room, tra-la,
Shit all around the room.

Mary in the kitchen shelling peas, shelling peas, shelling peas,
Mary in the kitchen shelling peas,
BULLSHIT!
Mary in the kitchen shelling peas,
The hairs of her cunt hung down to her knees,
Shit all around the room, tra-la,
Shit all around the room.

Mary in the garden sifting cinders, sifting cinders, sifting cinders,
Mary in the garden sifting cinders,
BULLSHIT!
Mary in the garden sifting cinders,
Blew one fart and broke ten windows,
Shit all around the room, tra-la,
Shit all around the room.

Mary had a dog whose name was Ben, name was Ben, name was Ben,
Mary had a dog whose name was Ben,
BULLSHIT!
Mary had a dog whose name was Ben,
Had one ball which worked like ten,
Shit all around the room, tra-la,
Shit all around the room.

Mary in the kitchen baking cakes, baking cakes, baking cakes,
Mary in the kitchen baking cakes,
BULLSHIT!
Mary in the kitchen baking cakes,
When out of the tits came two mild shakes,
Shit all around the room, tra-la,
Shit all around the room.

Mary Ann McCathy

Tune: Battle Hymn of the Republic

Mary Ann McCarthy, she went out to dig some clams,
Mary Ann McCarthy, she went out to dig some clams,
Mary Ann McCarthy, she went out to dig some clams,
But she didn't get one son of a bitchin' clam.
All she got was oysters,
All she got was oysters,
All she got was oysters,
And she never got one son of a bitchin' clam.

She dug up all the mud there was in San Francisco Bay,
She dug up all the mud there was in San Francisco Bay,
She dug up all the mud there was in San Francisco Bay,
And all she ever got was crabs.
All she ever got was crabs,
All she ever got was crabs,
All she ever got was crabs,
And she never got one son of a bitchin' clam.

She waded in the water till her ass it dug the sand,
She waded in the water till her ass it dug the sand,
She waded in the water till her ass it dug the sand,
But all she ever got was piles.
All she ever got was piles,
All she ever got was piles,
All she ever got was piles,

And she never got one son of a bitchin' clam.

She went to every party that the Army ever gave,
She went to every party that the Army ever gave,
She went to every party that the Army ever gave,
But all she ever got was clap,
All she ever got was clap,
All she ever got was clap,
All she ever got was clap,
And she never got one son of a bitchin' clam.

Mary Mac

There's a nice wee lass and her name is Mary Mac,
Make no mistake, she's the girl I'm gonna take
There's a lot of other chaps that wanna get up on her track,
But I'm thinking that they'd have to get up early.

Chorus:

Mary Mac's father's making Mary Mac marry me,
My father's making me marry Mary Mac,
I'm gonna marry Mary to get married and take care of me
And we'll all be making merry when I marry Mary Mac.

Now this wee lass she's got a lot of brass,
She's got a lot of gas, and her father thinks I'm class,
So I'd be a silly ass to let the matter pass,
Her father thinks she suits me pretty fairly.

Now Mary and her mother gain an awful lot together
In fact you never see the one without the other
And the fellows often wonder if it's Mary or the mother
Or the both of them together that I'm courtin'.

Now the wedding day's on Wednesday and everything's arranged
Her name will soon be changed to mine unless her mind be changed
And were making the arrangements and I'm just a bit deranged
For marriage is an awful undertakin'.
It's sure to be a grand affair and grander than a fair
There's gonna be a coach and pair for every couple there
We'll dine upon the finest fare I'm sure to get my share,
If I don't we'll all be very much mistaken.

Masturbation

Tune: Finicule Finecula

Last night, I stayed up late a-masturbating,
It felt so good--I knew it would.
All night, I stayed up late a-masturbating,
It felt so nice--I did it twice.

Oh, you should see me pulling on the long strokes,
It felt so grand--I used my hand.
Oh, you should see me pulling on the short strokes,
It felt so neat--I used my feet.

Beat it, smash it, throw it to the floor
Wrap it around the bed post, slam it in the door
Some ordinary folks I know would rather fornicate,
I just want to sit around the house and masturbate.

Mayor Of Bayswater's Daughter (The Hair On Her Dickie-Di-Do)

Tune: The Ash Grove

The Mayor of Bayswater
He has a lovely daughter,
And the hairs on her dickie-di-do
Hang down to her knees.

If she was my daughter
I'd have them cut shorter,
And the hairs on her dickie-di-do
Hang down to her knees.

Chorus:

To her knees, to her knees,
And the hairs on her dicky-di-do hang down to her knees.

I've smelt it, I've felt it,
It's just like a bit of velvet.
And the hairs on her dickie-di-do
Hang down to her knees.

I've seen it, I've tweened it,
I've been in-between it,
And the hairs on her dickie-di-do

Hang down to her knees.

'twould take a Brontosaurus
To lick her clitoris
And the hairs on her dickie-di-do
Hang down to her knees.

You'd need a coal miner,
To find her vagina
And the hairs on her dickie-di-do
Hang down to her knees.

She climbed on a mountain
And pissed like a bloody fountain,
And the hairs on her dickie-di-do
Hang down to her knees.

One black one, one white one,
And one with a bit of shit on,
And the hairs on her dicky-di-do,
Hang down to her knees.

I stroked 'em and poked 'em,
I rolled 'em and smoked 'em
And the hairs on her dickie-di-do
Hang down to her knees.

She stayed on a cattle ranch,
And came like a bloody avalanche
And the hairs on her dickie-di-do
Hang down to her knees.

She says she is not a whore,
But she bangs like a shithouse door
And the hairs on her dickie-di-do
Hang down to her knees.

She lives on malted milkshake,
And roots like a bloody rattlesnake
And the hairs on her dickie-di-do
Hang down to her knees.

She married an Italian,
With balls like a fucking stallion
And the hairs on her dickie-di-do
Hang down to her knees.

She divorced the Italian,
And married the stallion
And the hairs on her dickie-di-do
Hang down to her knees.

She married a Spaniard,
With a prick like a bloody lanyard
And the hairs on her dickie-di-do
Hang down to her knees.

She divorced the Spaniard,
And ran off with the bloody lanyard
And the hairs on her dickie-di-do
Hang down to her knees.

The aroma it lingers,
It smells like fish fingers
And the hairs on her dickie-di-do
Hang down to her knees.

She stayed in Seattle,
And went down on cattle
And the hairs on her dickie-di-do
Hang down to her knees.

Mayor Of Bayswater's Daughter - Variations

Tune: - The Ash Grove

*(*Variations* contributed by Flying Booger and ZiPpy, Pike's Peak H4 - hash verses by Flying Booger - in many hashes, the Chorus: is sung to honor the hares)*
(Take turns leading verses)

The Mayor of Bayswater,
He has a lovely daughter,
And the hairs on her dickie-di-doe,
Hang down to her knees.

Chorus:

Leader: And the hairs,
Pack: And the hairs,
Leader: And the hairs,
Pack: And the hairs,
Leader: And the hairs,

Pack: On her dicky-di-doe,
Hang down to her knees.
One black one, one white one,
And one with a bit of shite on,
And the hairs on her dicky-di-doe,
Hang down to her knees.

VARIATIONS
and one forty pound strength one
and one I caught a trout on
and one I found on a bar of soap
and one that blocked the storm drain
and one she used as dental floss
and one she uses for macramQ
and one dripping in olive oil
and one she towed my car with
and one that smelt of clitty litter
and one to start the mower with
and one they use in gunsights
and one with a drop of piss on
and one covered in algae
and one I start my outboard with
and one I broke a tooth on
and one I found in my mug of beer
and one the crabs are stuck on
and one she winched her Jeep with
and one she marked the trail with
and one she tied her Nikes with
and one she tied her whistle on
and one she roped the calves with
and one she pulled her trailer with
and one they hanged a horse thief with
and one she climbed a cliff with
and one she whipped the orphans with
etc . . .

VERSES:
I've smelt it, I've felt it,
It's just like a bit of velvet.

I could not believe my eyes,
When I peered down between her thighs.

I she were my daughter,
I'd have her cut them shorter.

I've seen it, I've seen it,
I've lain right in between it.

I stroked 'em and poked 'em,
I rolled 'em and smoked 'em.

You'd need a coal miner,
To find her vagina.

She lives on the mountain,
and pees like a bloody fountain.

She stayed on a cattle ranch,
And came like a bloody avalanche.

She says she is not a whore,
But she bangs like a shithouse door.

She lives on malted milkshake,
And roots like a bloody rattlesnake.

She married an Italian,
With balls like a fucking stallion.

She divorced the Italian,
And married the stallion.

She married a Spaniard,
With a prick like a bloody lanyard.

She divorced the Spaniard,
And ran off with the bloody lanyard.

The split of her beaver,
Looks just like June Cleaver's.
She slept with a demon,
Who drowned her with semen.

Her cat's name is Boris,
And it plays with her clitoris.

The aroma it lingers,
It smells like fish fingers.

She sat on the waterfront,
With the waves lapping up and down her cunt.

I've licked it and kissed it,
It tastes like a chocolate biscuit.

You can drive a Morris Minor,
Right up her vagina.

It was always hit-or-miss,
Whether I could find her clitoris.

She went to Arabia,
And got camel drool on her labia.

She stayed in Seattle,
And went down on cattle.

The light is so glitorous,
When it shines off her clitoris.

Her vagina was squishy,
And smelled a bit fishy.

She went with a Hash House Harrier,
Who fucked her but wouldn't marry her.

(MORE HASH VERSES, BY FLYING BOOGER):
She slept with a Hash House Harriette,
Who played melodies upon her clit.

She wooed the Grand Master,
But he couldn't satisfy her.

Grand Mattress gave her a go,
She used an electric dildo.
Three Joint Masters did sport in concert,
But they couldn't reach her G-spot.

She went out with the RA,
But he proved to be a lousy lay.

She seduced the Song Master,
But he couldn't outlast her.

Hare Raiser did sleep with her,
But got all tangled in her fur.

The hares swived her with great intent,

But they soon were limp and spent.

She depantsed the OnSec,
And scoffed at his tiny dick.

She rogered the Hash Scribe,
And begat an entire tribe.

She stripped for the Biermeister,
He shot off all over her.

Hash Shyster did groan, oh,
As he serviced her pro bono.

She gave head to the Hash Cash,
And he ejaculated in a flash.

The Chipmeister she tried to lay,
But he came during foreplay.

She mooned the Haberdasher,
Who fainted at the sight of her.

An SCB dove in her muff,
But found he hadn't tongue enough.

She said to the FRB,
"Do it doggie style with me."

The walkers were red and sore,
She shagged them right across the floor.

She had it off with a Ranger,
But he went DOT inside of her.

To a Whiner she took a shiner,
But he cried, "Any one but her."

She took on the entire pack,
She was hot but they were slack.

She was brisk with young ZiPpy,
But he came much too quickly.

So she tried Flying Booger,
But he couldn't get it up for her.

She had group sex with the Circle,
Next day our parts turned purple.

Men

Chorus:

(continuously):
Men, men, men, men, men, men, men, men . . .

Oh, it's fun to be on a ship with men,
And sail across the sea,
We don't know where we'll land, or when,
But still it's fun to be,
On a ship with men at sea.

There's men above and men below,
And men down in the galley.
There's Butch and Spike,
And Tom and Sam,
And one that we call Sally,
One that we call Sally (effeminately).

Oh, we are brave and we are bold,
And none of us are sissies.
Each night we lay down in our bunks,
And blow each other kissies (effeminately).

Miss Lee's Hoochie

Tune: Sweet Betsy from Pike

I went to Seoul City, and there met Miss Lee,
She said for a short time, oh come sleep with me.
We went to Lee's hoochie, a room with hot floors,
I left my shoes outside, and slid shut the door.

She took off her long johns, and rolled out the pad,
I gave her ten thousand, twas all that I had.
Her breath smelt of kimchee, her bosoms were flat,
No hair on her pussy, now how about that?

I asked to go benjo, she led me outside,
I reached for Old Smokey, he crawled back inside.
I rushed to the medics, cried "What shall I do?"

The doc was dumbfounded, Old Smokey was blue.

Now when you're in Seoul on your next three-day pass,
Don't go to Lee's hoochie, sit flat on your ass.
Now your ass may get blistered, and Lee may tempt you,
But better the red ass, then Old Smokey blue.

Molly Malone (Cockles And Mussels)

In Dublin's fair city, where the girls are so pretty,
I first set my eyes on sweet Molly Malone
As she wheeled her wheelbarrow
Through streets broad and narrow
Crying "Cockles and mussels, alive, alive oh!"

Chorus:
Alive, alive oh, alive, alive oh,
Crying:
Cockles and mussels, alive, alive oh!

She was a fishmonger and sure 'twas no wonder
For so were her mother and father before.
And they each wheeled their barrow through streets wide and narrow,
Crying "Cockles and mussels, alive, alive oh!"

She died of a fever and no one could save her
And that was the end of sweet Molly Malone.
Now her ghost wheels her barrow through streets wide and narrow,
Crying "Cockles and mussels, alive, alive oh!"

Monkey Farts

My father came here from Ireland,
He was quiet but they said that he was wise.
He and mother did their best, gave us a home and all the rest,
But to talk to us he never had the time.
Sure, he'd say "Pass the butter," or "Come here young man,"
Or "Keep quiet," or "No, you can't have a dime."
Until the day when I was leavin' when dad finally found a reason
For sharing his philosophy of life...

Chorus: He said "A monkey fart should smell like a banana,
An English fart should smell like cups of tea.

The farting of a fairy should be very light and airy,
When a father farts I hope you'll think of me.
An Irish fart should always lilt with laughter,
It should melt your heart and melt your shorts as well.
A lion's roars with power, cuckoos should fart every hour,
A nun's fart should have meaning but no smell.
A strong man's fart should sound out like a trumpet,
A pretty girl's should barely even squeak,
But the man that you can trust is the one who'd rather bust
Than ever let one slip right on the street.

Well, from my old man this really was an earful,
I tried to understand just what he meant;
His words were primitive but strong so I wouldn't get them wrong,
He was saying to be careful as I went.
He was saying to be happy as I could be,
He was saying watch my step and as I pass,
To beware who I look up to, and whetever else I might do,
Know that most of what you get from folks is just escaping gas...
Chorus:

Moose Song

Tune: Sweet Betsy from Pike

When I was a young lad I used to like girls,
I'd fondle their corsets and play with their curls,
But my true love ran off with a classmate named Bruce,
I never got treated that way by a moose.

Chorus:

> *Moose, moose, I likes a moose,*
> *I've never had anything quite like a moose,*
> *I've had lots of lovers, my life has been loose,*
> *But I've never had anything quite like a moose.*

When I'm in the mood for a very fine lay,
I go to the closet and pull out some hay,
I open the window and spread it around,
'Cause moose always come when there's hay on the ground.

Women like dresses and diamonds and cars,
I spend all my money on women in bars,
But a moose is content to be tied to a tree,
While I find other mooses to satisfy me.

Now gorillas are fine for a Saturday night,
And lions and tigers, they puts up a fight,
But it just ain't the same when you slams your caboose
As the feeling you gets when you humps with a moose.

I've done it with beasties with long flowing hair,
I'd do it with snakes if their fangs were not there,
I've made it with walrus, two ducks and a goose,
But I've never had anything quite like a moose.

I've tried many beasties on land or on sea
I've even tried hump-backs that humped back on me!
Sharks are quite good, tho they're hard to pull loose
But on dry land there is nothing quite like a moose!

Step in my study, and trophies you'll find
A black striped tiger and scruffy maned lion
You'll know the elephant by his ivory tooth
And the one that's a-winking, you know is the moose!

The lion succumbed to a thirty-ought-six
Machine guns and tigers I've proved do not mix
The elephant fell by a bomb with a fuse
But I won't tell a soul how I did in the moose!

Now I've broken the laws in this god-awful state
They've put me in prison and locked up the gate
They say that tomorrow I'll swing from a noose
But my last night I'll spend with a good sexy moose!

Well, now that I'm old and advanced in my years,
When I look at my past I'll shed me no tears,
As I sit in my rocker with a glass of Mateus,
Playing hide the salami with Millie the Moose!

Masturbating Man

Tune: Solitary Man

Melinda was mine, 'till the time that I found her,
Sucking Jim, blowing him. Then Sue came along,
Fucked me strong, that's what I thought.
Me and Sue...She blew too.

Don't know that I will, but until I can find me,

A girl who'll lay and won't play games behind me,
I'll be what I am… Masturbating Man.

I've had it to here, being where "FUCK's" a small word,
Part-time thing like the sting,
I know it's been done, fucking one girl that loves you,
Right or wrong, just screwing strong.

I'll be what I am… Masturbating Man.

My Father Was A Fireman

Clang, Clang
Bang, Bang… And the goddamn fire went out.
Oh, for the life of a fireman,
To ride on a fire engine red.
To say to a team of white horses,
GO AHEAD, GO AHEAD, GIVE ME HEAD….

My father was a fireman, he puts out fires
My brother was a fireman, he puts out fires
My sister Sal is a fireman's gal, she puts out – too.

My father was a taxicab driver, he goes downtown
My brother was a taxicab driver, he goes downtown
My sister Sal is a taxicab driver's gal, she goes down – too.

My father was a telephone repairman, he climbs up poles
My brother was a telephone repairman, he climbs up poles
My sister Sal is a telephone repairman's gal, she climbs poles – too

My father was a horticulturist, he pulls up roots
My bother was a horticulturist, he pulls up roots
My sister Sal is a horticulturist's gal, he pulls roots – too.

My father was an anesthesiologist, he passes gas
My brother was an anesthesiologist, he passes gas
My sister Sal was an anesthesiologist's gal, she farts a lot.

My father was an B-1 driver, he drives Hogs
My brother was an B-1 driver, he drives Hogs
My sister Sal was an B-1 driver's gal, she rides bone – too

My Name Is Jack

My name is Jack, tiddly ack, tiddly ack,
I'm a necrophilliac, tiddly ack, tiddly ack,
I fuck dead women
And I fill them full of semen
Oh do I get frustrated
When women get cremated
Burial's a must, 'cause you can't fuck dust!

Nancy Brown

Way out in West Virginia lived a gal named Nancy Brown,
You ain't never seen such beauty in a city nor a town,
Oh she lived up in the mountain,
Yes she lived up in the mountain,
Oh she lived up in the mountain mighty high.
And so it is related, not a bit contaminated,
She was as pure as the West Virginia sky.

Now there came the local cowboy with his guitar and his song,
He took Nancy to the mountain but she still knew right from wrong,
She came rollin' down the mountain,
She came rollin' down the mountain,
She came rollin' down the mountain mighty fine.
And despite that cowboy's urgin' she remained the village virgin,
She was as pure as the West Virginia sky.

Then there came the village deacon with his phrases sweet and kind,
He took Nancy to the mountain but she still could read his mind,
She came rollin' down the mountain,
She came rollin' down the mountain,
She came rollin' down the mountain mighty fine.
And they say that that there deacon didn't get what he was seekin',
She was as pure as the West Virginia sky.

But there came the city slicker with his thousand dollar bills,
He put Nancy in his Packard and drove up in them thar hills,
Oh they stayed up on the mountain,
She was laid upon the mountain,
Oh they stayed up on the mountain all that night.
She came down next mornin' early more a woman than a girl,
And her mother kicked the hussy out of sight.

Slow: Now the end of our ditty finds Nancy in the city,
And by all accounts she's doin' mighty swell,
For she's winin', and she's dinin',
And she's on her back reclinin',
And those West Virginia skies can go to hell.

Normal tempo: But there came the big Depression, caught our slicker by the pants,
He had to sell his Packard and give up his little Nance,
So she went back to the mountain,
Yes she went back to the mountain,
Oh she went back to the mountain mighty sore.
Now the cowboy and the deacon get the thing that they were seekin',
For she's nothing but a West Virginia whore.

No Balls At All

Tune: Sweet Betsy From Pike

Come all you young drunkards give ear to my tale,
I'll tell you a story that will make you turn pale,
It's about a young lady so pretty and small,
Who married a man who had no balls at all.
No balls at all, no balls at all,
She felt for his balls, he had no balls at all.

"Oh mother, oh mother, oh pity my luck,
I've married a man who's unable to fuck,
His toolbag is empty, his screwdriver's small,
The impotent wretch has got no balls at all."
No balls at all, no balls at all,
The impotent wretch has got no balls at all.

"My daughter, my daughter, don't be so sad,
I had the same problem with your dear old dad,
But there's many a man who'll give ear to the call,
Of the wife of a man who has no balls at all."
No balls at all, no balls at all,
To the wife of a man who has no balls at all.

The pretty young girl took her mother's advice,
And she thought the whole thing was exceedingly nice,
An eighteen pound baby was born in the fall,
But the poor little bastard had no balls at all.
No balls at all, no balls at all,
The poor little bastard had no balls at all.

None Is Bigger Than Mine

Three old whores from Baltimore
Were drinking sherry wine,
And one of them says to the other two,
"None is bigger than mine."

Chorus:

So haul on the sheets me hearties,
Sprinkle the decks with brine,
Bend to the oars, you lousy whores,
None is bigger than mine.

"You're a liar," said the second old whore,
"Mine's as big as the sea.
The ships sail in and the ships sail out,
With nary a tickle to me."

"You're a liar," said the third old whore,
"I've had me a thousand men.
There's some go by and there's some go in,
And there's some what never come out again."
"You're both liars," said the first old whore,
"Mine's as big as the air.
Why the sun could set in the crack of my cunt,
And never burn a pubic hair."

Nothing Could Be Finer

Nothing could be finer, than to be in your vagina, in the morning
Nothing could be sweeter, than your lips around my peter, in the morning.
If I had a wish, and let there be no doubt
I'd spend the whole night, fucking and sucking and eating you out
Oh, nothing could be finer, than to be in your vagina, in the morning.

Oh Beautiful

Tune: America is Beautiful

Oh Beautiful for spreading thigh,
For pubic patch of brown.
For four quart bosom majesty,
Bouncing up and down.

Oh Erica, oh Erica,
Now spread Your legs for me......
I'll bury my head in your furry bed,
Between Your spreading knees.

Oral Sex Is Good For You[1]

Tune: Camptown Races

Oral sex is good for you
Doo Dah, Doo Dah,
Oral sex is good for you, all the doo dah day
Gonna suck all night, gonna suck all day
'Cause oral sex is good for you, all the doo dah day.

Anal sex bugs my ass
Doo Dah, Doo Dah,
Anal sex bugs my ass, all the doo dah day
Cum between her eyes, cum between her thighs
'Cause anal sex bugs my ass, all the doo dah day.
Tit fucks are good for you
Doo Dah, Doo Dah,
Tit fucks are good for you, all the doo dah day
Cum between her lips, Cum between her tits
'Cause tit fucks are good for you, all the doo dah day.

Old King Cole

Old King Cole was a merry old soul, and a merry old soul was he,
He called for his wife in the middle of the night, and he called for his fiddlers three.
Now every fiddler had a very fine fiddle, and a very fine fiddle had he,
Fiddle diddle dee diddle dee, said the fiddlers,
What merry merry men are we,
There's none so fair as can compare,
With the ______________.

Old King Cole was a merry old soul, and a merry old soul was he,
He called for his wife in the middle of the night, and he called for his tailors three.
Now every tailor had a very fine needle, and a very fine needle had he,
Stick it in and out, in and out, said the tailors,
Fiddle diddle dee diddle dee, said the fiddlers,

---

1 **See „Fastmovers" from John Darrel Sherwood, Page 103.**

What merry merry men are we,
There's none so fair as can compare,
With the ________________.

The jugglers had two very fine balls: throw your balls in the air
The butchers had choppers: put it on the block, chop it off.
The barmaids had candles: pull it out, pull it out, pull it out.
The cyclists had pedals: round and round, round and round
The flutists had flutes: root diddly-oot-diddly-oot.
The painters had brushes: wop it up and down, up and down.
The horsemen had saddles: ride it up and down, up and down.
The carpenters had hammers: bang away, bang away, bang away.
The surgeons had knives: cut it round the knob, make it throb.
The parsons had very great alarm: goodness gracious me.
The fishermen had rods: mine is six feet long.
The huntsmen had horns: wake up in the morn with a horn.
The coalmen had sacks: want it in the front or the back?

Old King Cole (RAF Version)

Old King Cole was a merry old soul,
and a merry old soul was he,
He called for his wife in the middle of the night,
And he called for his pilots three.
And every pilot was a fine chap,
And a very fine chap was he.
"I don't give two fucks" said the pilots,
Merry merry men are we,
There's none so far as can compare to the boys of the RFC.

How's your father? ALL RIGHT!
How's your mother? SHE'S TIGHT!
How's your sister? SHE MIGHT!
When's the last time? LAST NIGHT!
When's the next time? TO-NIGHT!
Hail Britannia, with marmalade and jam,
Five Chinese crackers up your asshole,
BAM-BAM-BAM-BAM-BAM.

Old King Cole was a merry old soul,
and a merry old soul was he,
He called for his wife in the middle of the night,
And he called for his navigators three.
And every navigator was a fine chap,

And a very fine chap was he.
"Ten miles off our track" said the navigators,
"I don't give two fucks" said the pilots,
Merry merry men are we,
There's none so far as can compare to the boys of the RFC.

How's your father?	ALL RIGHT!
How's your mother?	SHE'S TIGHT!
How's your sister?	SHE MIGHT!
When's the last time?	LAST NIGHT!
When's the next time?	TO-NIGHT!

Hail Britannia, with marmalade and jam,
Four Chinese crackers up your asshole,
BAM-BAM-BAM-BAM...

Old King Cole was a merry old soul,
and a merry old soul was he,
He called for his wife in the middle of the night,
And he called for his engineers three.
And every engineer was a fine chap,
And a very fine chap was he.
"Port-side engine's out" said the engineers,
"Ten miles off our track" said the navigators,
"I don't give two fucks" said the pilots,
Merry merry men are we,
There's none so far as can compare to the boys of the RFC.

How's your father?	ALL RIGHT!
How's your mother?	SHE'S TIGHT!
How's your sister?	SHE MIGHT!
When's the last time?	LAST NIGHT!
When's the next time?	TO-NIGHT!

Hail Brittania, with marmelade and jam,
Three Chinese crackers up your asshole,
BAM...BAM...BAM

Old King Cole was a merry old soul,
and a merry old soul was he,
He called for his wife in the middle of the night,
And he called for his tail-gunners three.
And every tail-gunner was a fine chap,
And a very fine chap was he.
"RATA-TATA-RATA-TATA-TAT" said the tailgunners,
"Port-side engine's out" said the engineers,
"Ten miles off our track" said the navigators,
"I don't give two fucks" said the pilots,

Merry merry men are we,
There's none so far as can compare to the boys of the RFC.

How's your father? ALL RIGHT!
How's your mother? SHE'S TIGHT!
How's your sister? SHE MIGHT!
When's the last time? LAST NIGHT!
When's the next time? TO-NIGHT!
Hail Brittania, with marmelade and jam,
Two Chinese crackers up your asshole,
BAM…BAM…

Old King Cole was a merry old soul,
and a merry old soul was he,
He called for his wife in the middle of the night,
And he called for his adminers three.
And every adminer was a fine chap,
And a very fine chap was he.
"Nif-naf-nif-naf-naf" said the adminers,
"RATA-TATA-RATA-TATA-TAT" said the tailgunners,
"Port-side engine's out" said the engineers,
"Ten miles off our track" said the navigators,
"I don't give two fucks" said the pilots,
Merry merry men are we,
There's none so far as can compare to the boys of the RFC.

How's your father? ALL RIGHT!
How's your mother? SHE'S TIGHT!
How's your sister? SHE MIGHT!
When's the last time? LAST NIGHT!
When's the next time? TO-NIGHT!
Hail Brittania, with marmelade and jam,
One Chinese crackers up your asshole,
BAM!

Please Don't Burn The Shithouse Down

Please don't burn the shithouse down,
Mother's willing to pay.
My father's drunk and in the jail,
Sister's in a motherly way.
Brother dear is mighty queer,
Times are fucking hard
So please don't burn that shithouse down,

We'll all have to shit in the yard
Shit...in...the...yard!

Poetry

INTRO: You remember Old Mother Hubbard?
RESPONSE: I FUCKED HER!!!

Chorus:

Poetry, poetry. How do you like my poetry?
It may not be as mellow as Longfellow, but it's my poetry.

INTRO: Little Boy Blue...
REPONSE: HE NEEDED THE MONEY!!!

INTRO: Three blind mice, see how they run,
RESPONSE: WHERE THE FUCK ARE THEY GOING???

Rub a dub dub, three men in a tub. BUTT FUCKING!

Mary had a little lamb, its fleece was white as snow. It followed her to school one day, AND A BIG BLACK DOG FUCKED IT!

There once was a lady who lived in a shoe.
She had so many kids, HER CUNT FELL OUT!

Jack and Jill went up the hill, each with a buck and a quarter
Jill came down with two fifty, THE FUCKING WHORE!!

Jack and Jell went up the hill to fetch a pail of water.Jack fell down and broke his dick, SO JILL HAD TO MASTERBATE!

Little Miss Muffet, sat on a tuffet, eating her curds and whey.
Along came a spider, and sat down beside her And said "WHAT'S IN THE BOWL, BITCH!"
Old Mother Hubbard went to the cupboard, to fetch her dog a bone
But when she bent over, old Rover took over.
AND GAVE HER A BONE OF HIS OWN!

Little Jack Horner, sat in a corner, eating his sister away.
He stuck in his thumb and pulled out a plum
And said "WHERE'S YOUR CHERRY, BITCH!"

Hickory dickory dock, three mice ran up the clock.

The clock struck one AND KILLED THE LITTLE FUCKERS!!

Rock a by baby, in the treetop.
Your mother's whore AND I'M NOT YOUR POP!

Mary, Mary quite contrary
Shave that pussy CAUSE IT'S JUST TO HAIRY!

Hickory dickory dock, this chick was sucking my cock
The clock struck two, I blew my goo
AND I KICKED HER OUT ON THE NEXT BLOCK, WHAT A PIG!

Jack be nimble, Jack be quick
Jack's a fag CAUSE HE SUCKS DICK!

Mary, Mary quite contrary, how does your garden grow?
With silver bells and cockle shells, AND A GREAT BIG FUCKING CUCUMBER!

Georgie, Georgie puddin' and pie
Jerked off in his girlfriend's eye,
When her eye was dry and shut...
GEORGIE FUCKED THAT ONE EYED SLUT!!!

Jack sprat could eat no fat, his wife could eat no lean,
So jack ignored her flabby tits,
AND LICKED HER ASSHOLE CLEAN!!!

Pubic Hair

Tune: Baby Face

Pubic hairs, you've got the cutest little pubic hairs,
There's not another that can compare, pubic hairs,
Penis or Vagina, nothing can be finer.
Pubic hairs, I'm up in heaven when I'm in your underwear.
I didn't need a shovel to take a mouthful of you pretty pubic hairs!

Rhode Island Red

Tune: Itself

Has anybody seen my cock,
My big Rhode Island Red?

He's mostly pink, with a little bit of blue,
And he's purple on his head (Gor Blimey).
He stands straight up in the morning,
And he gives me wife a shock,
Has anybody seen, anybody seen,
Anybody, anybody seen my cock?

He's a right big-headed little upstart,
The best you've ever seen.
He could have got gonorrhea,
Instead he got gangrene.
He should have worn a condom,
But the silly sod forgot,
Has anybody seen, has anybody seen,
Has anybody seen my cock?

Roll Me Over The Clover

(Take turns leading verses)
Well, this is number one,
And the fun has just begun,
Roll me over, lay me down, and do it again.

Chorus:

Roll me over in the clover,
Roll me over, lay me down, and do it again.

Well, this is number two,
And my hand is on her shoe, etc

Well, this is number three,
And my hand is on her knee, etc

Well, this is number four,
And we're rolling on the floor, etc

Well, this is number five,
And the bee is in the hive, etc

Well, this is number six,
And she says she likes my tricks, etc

Well, this is number seven,
And we're in our seventh heaven, etc

Well, this is number eight,
And the nurse is at the gate, etc

Well, this is number nine,
And the twins are doing fine, etc

Well, this is number ten,
And we're at it once again, etc

Well, this is number eleven,
And we start again from seven, etc

Well, this is number twelve,
And she said, "You kan jag isalv," etc

Well, this is number twenty,
And she said that that was plenty, etc

Well, this is number thirty,
And she said that that was dirty, etc

Well, this is number forty,
And she said, "Now you are naughty," etc.

Roll Your Leg Over

Tune: Oh, Sally, My Dear

If all the young girls were like fish in the ocean,
I'd be a whale and I'd show them the motion.

Chorus:

> *Oh, roll your leg over, oh, roll your leg over,*
> *Roll your leg over the man in the moon.*

If all the young girls were like fish in a pool,
I'd be a shark with a waterproof tool.

If all the young girls were like fish in the brookie,
I'd be a trout and I'd get me some nookie.

If all the young girls were like winds on the sea,
I'd be a mainsail and let them blow me.

If all the young girls were like cows in the pasture,
I'd be a bull and I'd fill them with rapture.

If all the young girls were like mares in the stable,
I'd be a stallion and show them I'm able.

If all the young girls were like bricks in a pile,
I'd be a mason and lay them in style.

If all the young girls were like bells in a tower,
I'd be a clapper and bang them each hour.

If all the young girls were like telephone poles,
I'd be a squirrel and stuff nuts in their holes.

If all the young girls were like gals down in Sydney,
I ain't got much left but I've still got one kidney.

If all the young girls were like B-29s,
I'd be a jet fighter and buzz their behinds.

If all the young girls were like coals in a stoker,
I'd be a fireman and shove in my poker.

If all the young girls were like statues of Venus,
And I were equipped with a petrified penis.

If all the young girls were like Gypsy Rose Lee,
I'd be a G-string; oh boy, what I'd see.

If all the young girls were like sheep in the clover,
I'd be a ram and I'd ram them all over.

If all the young girls were like pancakes in Texas,
I'd be a Texan and eat them for breakfast.
If all the young girls were like grapes on the vine,
I'd be a plucker and have me a time.

If all the young girls were singing this song,
It'd be twice as dirty and five times as long.

If all the young girls were like trees in the forest,
I'd be a woodsman and climb their clitoris.

If all the young girls were like little white flowers
I'd be a bee and I'd suck them for hours.

If all the young girls were like linear spaces,

And I were a vector, I'd aim for their bases.

If all the young girls wore dresses with patches,
I'd tear off their patches to get at their snatches.

If all the young girls were vessels of clay
I'd be a potter and make them all day.

Sally In The Alley

Sally in the alley, sifting cinders
Lifts up her leg and farts like a man
The wind from her bloomers blew six windows
and the cheeks of her ass went
BAM! BAM! BAM!

Sam Hall

Ah me name it is Sam Hall,
Chimney sweep, chimney sweep,
Ah me name it is Sam Hall,
Chimney sweep.
Ah me name it is Sam Hall,
And I've robbed both rich and small.
And me neck will pay for all
When I die, when I die,
And me neck will pay for all
When I die.

I've got twenty pounds in store,
That's not all, that's not all,
I've got twenty pounds in store,
That's not all.
I've got twenty pounds in store
And I've robbed for twenty more.
For the rich must help the poor,
So must die, so must die,
For the rich must help the poor,
So must die.

Ah they brought me to Coote Hill
In a cart, in a cart,
Ah they brought me to Coote Hill
In a cart.

DEDICATION

This book contains our thoughts, our songs and our games. Lesser individuals who have never strapped their asses to a piece of flaming metal and hurled their bodies through the dead of night, skimming Terra Firma, will consider it of little or no redeeming social value. For this reason the contents of this book are held sacred by those of us who have: and need not concern those who do not and will not know what it means to fly a fighter.

For those gone, those here, and those yet to come, this book is our spirit and blood. If you fly a fighter, this book is for you....it is for us.

335 FIGHTER SQUADRON, "CHIEFS"

Ah they brought me to Coote Hill,
And 'twas there I made my will,
For the best of friends must part,
So must I, so must I,
For the best of friends must part,
So must I.

Up the ladder I did grope,
That's no joke, that's no joke,
Up the ladder I did grope,
That's no joke.
Up the ladder I did grope
And the hangman pulled the rope,
And it's ne'er a word I spoke,
Tumbling down, tumbling down,
And it's ne'er a word I spoke,
Tumbling down.

Sammy Small

Oh, my name is Sammy Small, fuck 'em all
Oh, my name is Sammy Small, fuck 'em all
Oh, my name is Sammy Small
And I've only got one ball
But it's better than none at all, so fuck 'em all

Oh, they say I killed a man, fuck 'em all
Oh, they say I killed a man, fuck 'em all
Oh, they say I shot him dead
With a piece of fucking lead
Now that silly fucker's dead, so fuck 'em all

Oh, they say I'm gonna swing, fuck 'em all
Oh, they say I'm gonna swing, fuck 'em all
Oh, they say I'm gonna swing
From a piece of fucking string
What a silly fucking thing, so fuck 'em all

Oh, the parson he will come, fuck 'em all
Oh, the parson he will come, fuck 'em all
Oh, the parson he will come
With his tales of kingdom come
He can shove it up his bum, so fuck 'em all

Oh, the sheriff will be there too, fuck 'em all
Oh, the sheriff will be there too, fuck 'em all

Oh, the sheriff will be there too
With his silly fucking crew
They've got fuck all else to do, so fuck 'em all

Oh, the hangman wears a mask, fuck 'em all
Oh, the hangman wears a mask, fuck 'em all
Oh, the hangman wears a mask
For his silly fucking task
He can shove it up his ass, so fuck 'em all

Oh, they say I greased the rope, fuck 'em all
Oh, they say I greased the rope, fuck 'em all
Oh, they say I greased the rope
With a piece of fucking soap
What a silly fuckin' joke, so fuck 'em all

I saw Molly in the crowd, fuck 'em all
I saw Molly in the crowd, fuck 'em all
I saw Molly in the crowd
And I felt so fucking proud
That I shouted right out loud JUST FUCK 'EM ALL!

Sammy Small (Vietnam version)

Oh, come round us fighter pilots, fuck 'em all,
Oh, come round us fighter pilots, fuck 'em all,
Oh, we fly the Goddamn plane,
Through the flak and through the rain,
And tomorrow we'll do it again,
So fuck 'em all.

Oh, they tell us not to think, fuck 'em all,
Oh, they tell us not to think, fuck 'em all,
Oh, they tell us not to think,
Just to dive and just to jink,
LBJ's a Goddamn fink,
So fuck 'em all.

Oh, we bombed Mu Gia Pass, fuck 'em all,
Oh, we bombed Mu Gia Pass, fuck 'em all,
Oh, we bombed Mu Gia Pass,
Though we only made one pass,

They really stuck it up our ass,
So fuck 'em all.

TACO Mission

The mission of the TACOS is to kill as many godless communist bastards and their subhuman cohorts as possible with the least expenditure of munitions and to restore cave dwellings as an accepted way of life in the former communist region.

David L. Quinlan, Maj. Gen. TACO

THE HARD AND FAST RULES OF DACT

*There is no need to check six since we have no ordnance that flies in that direction.

*No matter how cosmic you are, a lower wing loaded airplane will always give you a square corner.

*Excess energy is undesirable because you have to figure out something to do with it.

*PDCS weak dicks or Twin Tail Butt Pirates can loose the fight but win at the chalk board or have an excuse that will make your dick hard.

TACO SONGBOOK DISCLAIMER

If you don't like this songbook, or anything in it offends you, then piss off or go fuck yourself

GUSTOV the Magnificent

TACO

F-16

TACO

SONGBOOK

For Official Taco Use Only

Reproduced in May of 1995

„Taco" Songbook, 1995

Oh, we're on a JCS, fuck 'em all,
Oh, we're on a JCS, fuck 'em all,
Oh, they sent the whole damn wing,
Probably half of us will sing,
What a silly fucking thing,
So fuck 'em all.

Oh, we lost our fucking way, fuck 'em all,
Oh, we lost our fucking way, fuck 'em all,
Oh, we strafed Goddamn Hanoi,
Killed every fucking girl and boy,
What a Goddamn fucking joy,
So fuck 'em all.

Oh, my bird got all shot up, fuck 'em all,
Oh, my bird got all shot up, fuck 'em all,
Oh, my bird it did get shot,
And I'll probably cry a lot,
But I think that it's Shit Hot!
So fuck 'em all.

Scotland The Brave

Hark when the night is falling
Hear! hear the pipes are calling,
Loudly and proudly calling,
Down thro' the glen.
There where the hills are sleeping,
Now feel the blood a-leaping,
High as the spirits of the old Highland men.

Chorus:

Towering in gallant fame, Scotland my mountain home,
High may your proud standards gloriously wave,
Land of my high endeavour,
Land of the shining river, Land of my heart for ever,
Scotland the brave.

High in the misty Highlands,
Out by the purple islands,
Brave are the hearts that beat
Beneath Scottish skies.
Wild are the winds to meet you,
Staunch are the friends that greet you,
Kind as the love that shines from fair maiden's eyes.

Far off in sunlit places,
Sad are the Scottish faces,
Yearning to feel the Kiss
Of sweet Scottish rain.
Where tropic skies are beaming,
Love sets the heart a-dreaming,
Longing and dreaming for the homeland again.

Seven Drunken Nights

As I went home on Monday night,
As drunk as drunk could be,
I saw a horse outside the door
Where my old horse should be.
I called my wife and I said to her:
"Will you kindly tell to me,
Who owns that horse outside the door,
Where my old horse should be."

Chorus:

Ah, you're drunk, you're drunk, you silly old fool,
And still you cannot see,
That's a lovely sow that
My mother sent to me."
Well, it's many a day I've travelled
A hundred miles or more,
But a saddle on a sow, sure I never saw before.

As I went home on Tuesday night,
As drunk as drunk could be,
I saw a coat behind the door
Where my old coat should be.
I called my wife and I said to her:
"Will you kindly tell to me,
Who owns that coat behind the door,
Where my old coat should be."

Chorus:

As I went home on Wednesday night,
As drunk as drunk could be,
I saw a pipe upon the chair
Where my old pipe should be.
I called my wife and I said to her:
"Will you kindly tell to me,
Who owns that pipe upon the chair,
Where my old pipe should be."

Chorus:

As I went home on Thursday night,
As drunk as drunk could be,
I saw two boots beside the bed
Where my old boots should be.
I called my wife and I said to her:
"Will you kindly tell to me,
Who owns those boots beside the bed
Where my old boots should be."

Chorus:

As I went home on Friday night,
As drunk as drunk could be,
I saw a head upon the bed
Where my old head should be.

I called my wife and I said to her:
"Will you kindly tell to me,
Who owns that head upon the bed,
Where my old head should be."

Chorus:

As I went home on Saturday night,
As drunk as drunk could be,
I saw two hands upon her breasts
Where my old hands should be.
I called to my wife and I said to her:
"Will you kindly tell to me,
Who's hands are those upon your breasts
Where my old hands should be."

Chorus:

As I went home on Sunday night,
As drunk as drunk could be,
I saw a cock inside my wife
Where my old cock should be.
I called my wife and I said to her:
"Will you kindly tell to me,
Who's cock is that inside your twat,
Where my old cock should be?"

> *Ah, you're drunk, you're drunk, you silly old fool,*
> *And still you cannot see,*
> *That's a super absorbant tampon that*
> *My mother sent to me."*
> *Well, it's many a day I've travelled*
> *A hundred miles or more,*
> *But testicles on a tampon, sure I never saw before.*

Seven Old Ladies

Tune: Oh My, What Can the Matter Be?

Chorus: Oh dear, what can the matter be?
Seven old ladies locked in the lavat'ry,
They were there from Sunday to Saturd'y,
Nobody knew they were there.

They said they were going to have tea with the Vicar,
They went in together, they thought it was quicker,

But the lavat'ry door was a bit of a sticker,
And the Vicar had tea all alone.

The first was the wife of a deacon in Dover,
And thought she was known as a bit of a rover,
She liked it so much she thought she'd stay over,
And nobody knew she was there.

The next old lady was old Mrs. Bickle,
She found herself in a desperate pickle,
Shut in a pay booth, she hadn't a nickel,
And nobody knew she was there.

The next was the Bishop of Chichester's daughter,
She went in to pass some superfluous water,
She pulled on the chain and the rising tide caught her,
And nobody knew she was there.

The next old lady was Abigale Humphrey,
Who settled inside to make herself comfy,
And then she found out she could not get her bum free,
And nobody knew she was there.

The next old lady was Elizabeth Spender,
Who was doing all right till a vagrant suspender,
Got all twisted up in her feminine gender,
And nobody knew she was there.

The last was a lady named Jennifer Trim,
She only sat down on a personal whim,
But she somehow got pinched 'twixt the cup and the brim,
And nobody knew she was there.

But another old lady was Mrs. McBligh,
Went in with a bottle of booze on the sly,
She jumped on the seat and fell in with a cry,
And nobody knew she was there.

She'll Be Right

When you're hunting in the mountains and your dog's put up a chase,
And a porker's coming at you and he doesn't like your face,
And you're running and he's running and he's pounding on the pace,
Well, don't worry mate, she'll be right.

She'll be right, mate, she'll be right.
Don't worry, mate, she'll be right.
You can get your feed of pork when he slows down to a walk,
So don't worry, mate, she'll be right.

When you're logging in the ranges and you're riding down the bluff,
With forty feet of timber riding right behind your chuff,
Your clutch has started slipping and your brakes are worse than rough,
Well, don't worry mate, she'll be right.
She'll be right, mate, she'll be right.
Don't worry, mate, she'll be right.
Just give her all you can give her, and she'll fly into the river,
So don't worry, mate, she'll be right.

When they've finished off your forwards, and your backs are wearing thin,
The second half's near over and you've forty points to win,
And a hulking wing three quarter's got his teeth stuck in your shin,
Well, don't worry mate, she'll be right.

She'll be right, mate, she'll be right.
Don't worry, mate, she'll be right.
You won't worry who'se the loser when you meet them down the boozer,
So don't worry, mate, she'll be right.

When you're boiling up the copper and you're brewing up the hops
You've made a hundred dozen and you've hammered down the tops,
The misses comes and asks you where you've put your footy socks,
Well, don't worry mate, she'll be right.

She'll be right, mate, she'll be right.
Don't worry, mate, she'll be right.
Shove a shot of metho in, and you'll swear you're drinking gin,
So don't worry, mate, she'll be right.

Sit On My Face

Sit on my face and tell me that you love me
I'll sit on your face and tell you I love you too
I love to hear you o-ra-lise
When I'm between your thighs
You blow me away.
Sit on my face and let my lips embrace you
I'll sit on your face and then I'll love you truly

Life can be fine if we both sixty nine
If we sit on our faces
In all sorts of places
And play till we're blown away.

Sit On My Face (RAF)

Oh, would you like to sit on my face,
spread your ass all over the place,
put my nose in a fragrant place,
or would you rather suck my hog!

Some Die Of Drinking Water

Tune: British Grenadier

Some die of drinking water,
And some of drinking beer,
Some die of constipation,
And some of diarrhea.
But of all the world's diseases,
There's none that can compare,
With the drip, drip, drip of the syphilitic prick
Of a British Grenadier.

When he goes forth in battle,
His weapon in his hand,
The lasses fall like cattle,
There's none can make a stand.
But when the campaign's over,
It's then he feels so queer,
With the drip, drip, drip of the syphilitic prick
Of a British Grenadier.

And when he does retire,
To take his well-earned rest,
There burns an ancient fire,
To do what he does best.
And yet, the truth is bitter,
There's one thing he does fear,
It's the drip, drip, drip of the syphilitic prick
Of a British Grenadier.

I like the girls who say they will,

And I like the girls who won't.
I hate the girls who say they will,
And then they say they don't.
But of all the girls I like the best,
I may be wrong or right,
Are the girls who say they never will,
But look as though they might.

Son's Coming Home

Tune: the Camptown Races

Son's coming home in a body bag, doo-dah, doo-dah,
Son's coming home in a body bag, oh doo-dah-day

Chorus:

Motherfucker's dead, never found his head
Son's coming home in a body bag, oh doo-dah-day

Got shot down by an SA-2, doo-dah, doo-dah,
Got shot down by an SA-2, oh doo-dah-day

Tried to punch out way too late, doo-dah, doo-dah,
Tried to punch out way too late, oh doo-dah-day

Now he's just a blob of goo, doo-dah, doo-dah,
Now he's just a blob of goo, oh doo-dah-day

SuperCallousFlagellisticsExpectCunnilingus

Tune: Supercallifragilisticexpecalidosious

Chorus:

Supercallousflagellisticsexpectcunnilingus,
Queers like to take it up the bum from dildoes, dicks, or fingers,
Lesbians like their tonguing slow to make the climax linger,
But Supercallousflagellisticsexpectcunnilingus,
Um-diddle-diddle-diddle, Um-diddleye

My fat Auntie Ethel was into suits of rubber,
Then she met the Michelin Man and took him as a lover,
But they used a diesel tube for enemas on each other,
The explosion rocked the city hall and covered it in blubber.
Um-diddle-diddle-diddle, Um-diddleye

Uncle John likes whips and chains and ladies to disfigure,
Auntie Kath liked to be tied and whipped with bamboo canes or wicker,
She said, "Whip me, whip me, and make me writhe and slither,"
He said, "No, I'll tickle you, that will make my dick get stiffer."
Um-diddle-diddle-diddle, Um-diddleye

Uncle Cyril, we always knew, was into brown battery,
He stuck a dildo up his boyfriend's bum with lots of beer and flattery,
"Take it out and I'll give you dick," he said quite matter of factly,
"Oh no, please don't take it out but kindly change the battery!"
Um-diddle-diddle-diddle, Um-diddleye

Mary Jane looks like a man but on little girls she's keener,
Thought she'd take a virgin home and try to get between her,
The virgin said, "Oh no please sir, I don't know where it's been, sir,"
Mary Jane said, "It's factory fresh," and introduced a wiener.
Um-diddle-diddle-diddle, Um-diddleye.

Sweet Mad Dog Wine

Tune: Sweet Caroline

Where it began
I can recall no longer
but then I know its stronger still.
Spewed in the can
then raised another fist of
fizzy, fermented twist-off swill.

Young,
freshly wrung,
Cheap and strong,
on my tongue,
chug it in--

Sweet Mad Dog wine
what goes down must come back up
I'm drinking blind
looking for a plastic cup,
oh, fuck it

I'll drink it straight
out of the bottle, too late
to realize I've had too much
Isn't it great

I've lost my sense of reason
and now I've lost my sense of touch

Warm,
feeling warm,
freezing cold,
now I'm warm
once again

Sweet Mad Dog wine
good times shouldn't taste like wood
I'm in a bind
'cause I puked up all my food,
oh, fuck, it

(repeat last)

Tampax Factory

Tune: The Caissons Go Rolling Along

You can tell by bulging that she hasn't been indulging,
When the end of the month comes around,
You can tell by the string that is hanging from her thing,
That the end of the month is around.

And it's: Hey, Ho Hee in the Tampax factory,
Sing your orders loud and clear,
Large, medium, small, junior Miss and Family size.

You can tell from the hum that is coming from her bum,
That the end of the month is around,
You can tell from the moanin' that she's short of haemoglobin,
When the end of the month comes around.

And it's: Hey, Ho Hee in the Tampax factory,
Sing your orders loud and clear,
Large, medium, small, junior Miss and Family size.

You can tell by the smell that she isn't very well,
When the end of the month comes around.
You can tell by the stink that she isn't in the pink,
When the end of the month comes around.

And it's: Hey, Ho Hee in the Tampax factory,

Sing your orders loud and clear,
Large, medium, small, junior Miss and Family size.

The Alcoholic's Anthem

Tune: Men Of Harlech

What's the use of drinking tea
indulging in sobriety?
(and) tee-total perversity?
It's healthier to booze!

What's the use of milk and water?
these are drinks that never oughter
be allowed in any quarter
Come on, lose your Blues!

Mix yourself a Shandy!
Drown yourself in brandy!
A Sherry sweet, a Whiskey neat,
or any kind of likker that is handy!

There's no blinking sense in drinking
any thing that doesn't make you stinking
There's no happiness like sinking
blotto to the floor!

Put an end to all frustration
drinking may be your salvation
end it all in dissipation
rotten to the core!

Aberrations metabolic
Ceilings that are hyperbolic
these are for the Alcoholic
lying on the floor!

Vodka for the arty
Gin, to make you hearty!
Lemonade was only made
for drinking if your mother's at the party!

So stay clear of home-made beer
and anything that isn't labeled "clear"
There is nothing else to fear!

Bottoms up, my boys!

The Ancient And Old Irish Condom

Tune: Rosin the Beau

I was up to me arse in the muck, Sir,
with a peat contract down in the bog
When me shovel it struck something hard, Sir,
that I thought was a rock or a log
T'was a box of the finest old oak, Sir,
T'was a foot long, and four inches wide
and not giving a damn for the Fairies
I just took a quick look inside

Now I opened the lid of this box, Sir,
and I swear that my story is true
T'was an ancient and old Irish condom
A relic of Brian Boru

T'was an ancient and old Irish condom
a foot long and made of elk hide,
With a little gold tag on it's end, Sir,
with his name, rank, and stud fee inscribed

Now, I cast me mind back thru the ages
To the days of that horny old Celt
With his wife lyin' by on the bed, Sir,
As he stood by the fire in his pelt

And I thought that I heard Brian whisper
As he stood in the fire's rosy light
"Well, you've had yer own way long enough, dear...
'Tis the hairy side outside, tonight."

T'was an ancient and old Irish condom
a foot long and made of elk hide,
With a little gold tag on it's end, Sir,
with his name, rank, and stud fee inscribed.

The Balls Of O'Leary

The Balls of O'Leary
Are wrinkled and hairy,

They're stately and shapely
Like the dome of St. Paul's.
The women all muster
To see that great cluster,
Oh, they stand and they stare
At the mighty red pair
Of O'Leary's Balls!

The Banks Of The Roses

Chorus: On the banks of the roses my love and I sat down
And I took out a fiddle for to play my love a tune
In the middle of the tune, oh, she sighed and she said
Young Johnny, lovely Johnny, would you leave me?

When I was just a young lad, I heard my father say
I'd sooner see you dead and buried in the clay
Rather than be married to any runaway
On the lovely sweet banks of the roses.

Oh, then I am a runaway and soon I'll let you know
That I can drink a bottle and drink with anyone
And if her father doesn't like me, he can keep his daughter home
Then Johnny will go roving with another.

If ever I get married 'twill be in the month of May
When the leaves they are green and the meadows they are gay
And me and my true love will sit and sport and play
By the lovely sweet banks of the roses.

The Bantam Cock

He was a fine upstanding bantam-cock
So brisk, and stiff, and spry...
With a springy step, and a jaunty plume,
And a purposeful look in his eye
In his little black laughing eye!

So I took him to the coop and introduced him to
My seventeen wide-eyed hens
And he tupped and he tupped as a hero tupps,
And he bowed to them all, and then,
He up and took 'em all again!

Then upon the peace of my ducks and geese
He boldly did intrude
And with glazed eyes and opened mouths
They bore him with fortitude...
And a little bit of gratitude!

He jumped my giggling guinea-fowl!
He thrust his attentions upon
Twenty hysterical turkeys,
And a visiting migrant swan!
And the bantam thundered on!

He groped my fan-tail pigeon doves,
My lily-white Columbine,
And as I was lookin' at me budgerigar,
He jumped my parrot from behind!
And it was sittin' on me shoulder at the time!

But all of a sudden, with a gasp and a gulp,
He clapped his wings to his head!
He lay flat on his back with his feet in the air;
My bantam-cock was dead!
And the vultures circled overhead!

What a noble beast! What a champion cock!
What a way to live and die!
As I dug him a grave to protect his bones,
From those hungry buzzards in the sky,
The bantam opened up his eyes!

He gave me a wink, and a terrible grin,
The way that rapists do....
He said, "Do you see them silly daft buggers up there?
They'll be down in a minnit 'er two!
They'll be down in a minnit 'er two!"

The Ball (The Death of 69,000)

Group: Twas the night of the King's castration, and the King was throwing a ball...his left one. Counts, Discounts, and No-Accounts were seated at the table, shooting camel shit, for bullshit was unknown.

Queen: Balls!

Group: Cried the Queen.

Queen: If I had two, I'd be King.

Group: The King chuckled, not that he had to, but he had two. Up rode David on his dashing white steed. Up rode the King on his diamond studded jockstrap.

David: Where's the Princess?

Group: Cried David.

King: She's in bed with Diptheria.

Group: Said the King.
David: What?!!

Group: Cried David.

David: Is that Greek bastard back in town?

Group: And he was thrown to the lions for insolence. But the Lions couldn't hurt him, they hadn't won a game in years. But the Lions rose up anyway, and David grabbed one by the left nut.

Lion: That tickles!

Group: Said the Lion.

David: What tickles?

Group: Said David.

Lion: Testicles.

Group: Said the lion. And David was summoned to come forth. But David wanted to come first, so he tried to sneak to the front of the line. As he snuck around, he slipped on some camel shit. Shit flew at Random, Random ducked, and the shit hit the king in the face.

King: Shit!

Group: Said the King. And 69,000 squatted and groaned.

David: Where's the princess?

Group: Asked David.

King: Fuck the princess!

Group: Said the King. And 69,000 were trampled to death, for the King's word was law.

The Ballad of Yukon Pete

Well grab a glass and pull up a seat,
And I'll tell you a story of Big Ass Lil and Yukon Pete.

Lil was the village queen,
The fuckenest whore you've ever seen,
While most girls fucked with grace and ease,
Lil blew dick like the summer breeze.

But when she fucked, she fucked for keeps,
She piled her victims up in heaps.
And there was a rumor going around that town,
That no man could pull Lil's ass down.

But way up north where the twin rivers meet,
Lived a one balled half breed named Yukon Pete.
Now Pete was a dirty motherless soul,
Who fucked bear, sheep, and woodchuck holes.
And when he got a whiff of Big Ass Lil,
He packed up his rubbers and came down from the hill.

He strode into town on size thirty-two feet,
Dragging sixteen yards of that red hot meat.
Well the scene was set at windy mill,
By the brick shithouse high on the hill.
All the ladies gathered for a ringside seat,
Just to watch that halfbreed sink his meat.

Well they fucked and they fucked and they fucked for hours,
Uprooting trees, shrubs and flowers.
Lil did front flips, back flips, and other stunts,
All unknown to most common cunts.
But Pete caught on to every trick and just kept pumping in more dick.

Then Lil gave Pete that whorehouse squeeze,
Dropping that halfbreed down to his knees.

But Pete came back with a Yukon grunt,
That popped out her eyes and split open her cunt.

Well Lil rolled over, farted twice, then sighed,
She said, "Boys, I've been fucked," farted once more and died.

Well Lil had a sister named Tight Twat Tina,
Who was a little slimmer but a whole lot meaner.
She saddled her mule and rode into town,
Stopped in the square and pulled her pants down.

She said, "Where's that bastard they call Yukon Pete?
It's time for his dick to go down in defeat.
You fucked Lil to death and you called her a whore,
but now it is time that I even the score."
Well, Pete heard the challengeand he rode to the square,
And he found Tina there just a scratching her hair.
So he pulled down his pants and he pumped in a load,
Knocking that bitch right into the road.
But Tina got up and just shook off the sperm,
And said, "Not bad, boy, but now it's my turn."

She grabbed his cock and gave it a twist,
A fresh wad of cream oozed into her fist.
She stoked it with fury, she stoked it with lust,
She made him keep cumming until there was dust.

Well Pete tried for a hard-on, but his pecker was limp,
And all the ladies said, "Look, girls, Yukon Shrimp."
Yes, Pete was a howlin' and holdin' his balls,
But he said this is only the first of three falls.

He pumped up his pecker and aimed for her slit,
But even with a crowbar, ain't no way it would fit.
So he spit in his hand and he greased up his pole,
And he aimed it once more for her tight little hole.

But Tina just laid down and rolled over in the street,
Leaving Pete standing there slapping his meat.
"Roll over," yelled Pete. "I'll be fucked if I do," said Tina,
"You'll be cornholed if you don't," said Pete.

And cornholed she was, by a yard of Yukon cock,
When Pete was done humping, her intestines were shocked!
When all the boys asked him about his temendous feat,
He said, "Boys, I'm heading back up to the Yukon to beat my meat."

The Cuckoo

Tune: Itself

The cuckoo is a funny bird,
Who sits in the grass,
With his wings neatly folded,
And his beak up his ass.
In this strange position,
He can only say, "Twit!"
'Cause it's hard to say, "Cuckoo,"
With a beak full of shit.

The Duchess Was A-Dressing

The duchess was a-dressing,
A-dressing for the ball,
When out the window she did spy him
Pissing on the wall…

Chorus:

> *With that lily-white kidney wiper,*
> *And balls the size of three,*
> *And a half a yard of foreskin*
> *Hanging down below his knees*
> *Hanging down, (echo: What a prick!)*
> *Swinging free, (echo: Inches thick!)*
> *With his yard and a half of foreskin*
> *Hanging down below his knee.*

The duchess wrote a letter
And in it she did say,
"I'd rather be fucked by you
Than by his lordship any day"

So he mounted up his charger,
And on it he did ride
With his balls slung over his shoulder
And his cock hung by his side

He rode into the courtyard,
He rode into the hall,
My goodness cried the butler,
He's come to fuck us all.

He fucked the cook in the kitchen
He fucked the maidens all,
He even fucked the butler
Who was the randiest bugger of all.

Well he mounted up his charger
And rode into the street,
With little drops of semen
Pitter-patter at his feet

They say he's dead by long now,
And buried in St Pauls,
They say it took four and twenty men
To carry both his balls.

Some say he went to heaven,
Some say he went to hell,
Some say he fucked the devil,
If he did he fucked him well.

The Dunne's Song

I was once well acquainted with a man called Joseph Dunne,
A very respectable sort of a man and fond of harmless fun,
He courted young and married was when he was twenty-one,
And a very respectable family had Mr. and Mrs. Dunne.

Chorus:

For there was High Dunne and Low Dunne, Under Dunne and Over Dunne,
All the other younger Dunnes, in and out they run;
Ther was oul' Dunne and young Dunne, and young Dunne's youngest son;
Young Dunne will be a Dunne when the elder Dunne is done.

In the course of time this Joseph Dunne he found himself a wife,
And soon he found he had to fight the hardest fight of life:
To keep ten little bellies full, and a wife that weighed a ton,
To any man who can do all that, you have to say, "Well done!"

When Mrs. Dunne presented Dunne with their first strapping son,
they named him Michael Patrick Dunne but called him Cherry Plum,
And when the price of bread went up, and more children did come,
Said Mrs. Dunne to Mr. Dunne, "More bread or we'll be done."

So here's to the youngest son of Dunne, likewise to the eldest Dunne,
And here's to the youngest son of Dunne when the eldest Dunne is done,
For any man can be well done in this big wicked world,
What's done by Dunne must be well-done, so well done good oul' Dunne!

The Engineer's Song

The engineer told me before he died,
Ah-rump titty rump titty rump titty rump
The engineer told me before he died,
And I've no reason to believe he lied
Ah-rump titty rump titty rump titty rump
Rump titty rump titty rump titty rump

He had a wife with a cunt so wide,
Ah-rump titty rump titty rump titty rump
He had a wife with a cunt so wide,
That she could not be satisfied
Ah-rump titty rump titty rump titty rump
Rump titty rump titty rump titty rump

So he built a cock of steel,
Ah-rump titty rump titty rump titty rump
So he built a cock of steel,
With two brass balls and a big red wheel
Ah-rump titty rump titty rump titty rump
Rump titty rump titty rump titty rump

Then he filled those balls with cream
Ah-rump titty rump titty rump titty rump
Then he filled those balls with cream,
And the great machine was driven by steam
Ah-rump titty rump titty rump titty rump
Rump titty rump titty rump titty rump

Round and round went the big red wheel,
Ah-rump titty rump titty rump titty rump
Round and round went the big wheel,
And in and out went the cock of steel
Ah-rump titty rump titty rump titty rump
Rump titty rump titty rump titty rump

Higher and higher went the level of steam,

Ah-rump titty rump titty rump titty rump
Higher and higher went the level of steam,
And down and down went the level of cream
Ah-rump titty rump titty rump titty rump
Rump titty rump titty rump titty rump

Then at last the maiden cried,
Ah-rump titty rump titty rump titty rump
Then at last the maiden cried,
"Enough, Enough, I'm satisfied"
Ah-rump titty rump titty rump titty rump
Rump titty rump titty rump titty rump

Now we come to the tragic bit,
Ah-rump titty rump titty rump titty rump
Now we come to the tragic bit,
There was no way of stopping it
Ah-rump titty rump titty rump titty rump
Rump titty rump titty rump titty rump

She was split from ass to tit,
Ah-rump titty rump titty rump titty rump
She was split from ass to tit,
And the great machine was covered in shit
Ah-rump titty rump titty rump titty rump
Rump titty rump titty rump titty rump!

The Finest Fucking Family In The Land

There's a gentlemen's convenience in the north of Waterloo
And another for the ladies further down,
For a penny on deposit you can hire a water closet
But a season ticket costs you half a crown.
Have you met my Uncle Hector, he's a cock and ball inspector
At a celebrated English public school,
And my brother sells French letters and a patent cure for wetters
We're a fucking queer collection, ain't it cruel?

Life presents a dismal picture, Father has ureathral stricture
And Granny's down with epileptic fits
Grandpa's just now been deported and dear Annie's been aborted
And all of us are yelling "bloody quits!"
Henry has no occupation save excessive masturbation
And cracking ice for Father's piles, no doubt,

But we will not be down-hearted, although Auntie has just farted
And blown her bloody asshole inside-out

When you wake up in the morning with your hands upon your knees
And the shadow of your pecker on the wall,
And the hair are growing thick between your asshole and your prick
While the rats are playing snooker with your balls
Have you met my sister Tilly? She's a whore in Picadilly,

And my mother is another in the Strand.
And my father sells his arsehole to the guards at Windsor Castle,
We're the finest fucking family in the land.

The Gay Caballero

Tune: The Gay Caballero

Oh, I am a gay caballero,
Going from Rio de Janeiro,
With an exceedingly long latraballee,
And two fine latraballeros.

I went down to Tijuana,
Exceedingly fine Tijuana,
With my exceedingly long latraballee,
And my two fine latraballeros.

I met a gay senorita,
Exceedingly gay senorita,
She wanted to play with my latraballee,
And with one of my latraballeros.

Oh, now I've got the clapito,
Exceedingly painful clapito,
Right on the end of my latraballee,
And on one of my latraballeros.

I went to see a medico,
Exceedingly fine medico,
He looked at the end of my latraballee,
And at one of my latraballeros.

He took out a long stiletto,
Exceedingly long stiletto,
He cut off the end of my latraballee,

And one of my latraballeros.

And now I'm a sad caballero,
Returning to Rio de Janiero,
Minus the end of my latraballee,
And one of my latraballeros.

At night I lay on my pillow,
Seeking to finger my willow,
All I find there is a handful of hair,
And one dried-up latraballero.

The Good Ship Venus

Aboard the good ship Venus,
By God, you should have seen us,
The figurehead, a whore in bed,
The mast, a throbbing penis.

Chorus: There was friggin' in the riggin',
Wankin' on the plankin',
Masturbatin' on the gratin',
There was fuck all else to do.

The first mate's name was Paul,
He only had one ball,
But with that cracker he rolled terbaccer
Around the cabin wall.

His cabin boy was Kipper,
A dirty little nipper,
They stuffed his ass with broken glass,
And circumcised the skipper.

The second mate's name was Andy,
His dick was long and bandy,
They filled his ass with molten brass
For pissing in the brandy.

The third mate's name was Morgan,
He was a grisly Gorgon,
Three times a day he strummed away
Upon his sexual organ.

The cox'n's name was Slugger,
He was a dirty bugger,
He wasn't fit to shovel shit
On any bugger's lugger.

A cook whose name was Freeman,
He was a dirty demon,
He fed the crew on menstrual stew
And hymens fried in semen.

Another cook was O'Malley,
He didn't dilly-dally,
He shot his bolt with such a jolt
He whitewashed half the galley.

The bosun's name was Lester,
He was a hymen tester,
Through hymens thick he shoved his dick
And left it there to fester.

The engineer was McTavish,
And young girls he did ravish,
He lost his tool in Istanbul,
He was a little lavish.

The bosun's mate was Carter,
By God, he was a farter,
When the wind wouldn't blow and the ship wouldn't go,
We'd get Carter the farter to start 'er.

A homo was the purser,
He couldn't have been worser,
With all the crew he had a screw,
Until they yelled, "Oh no, sir!"

Another one was Cropper,
Oh Christ, he had a whopper,
Twice round the deck, once round his neck,
And up his bum for a stopper.

The ship's dog's name was Rover,
The whole crew did him over,
They ground and ground the wretched hound
From Lisbon to Andover.

Twas on the broad Atlantic,

Where the water's almost static,
The rise and fall of cock and balls
Was almost automatic.

The captain's wife was Mabel,
And whenever she was able,
She gave the crew its daily screw
Upon the galley table.

The skipper's daughter Mabel,
They fucked when they were able.
They tacked those tits, the dirty shits,
Right to the galley table.

The skipper's other daughter,
They tossed into the water.
Delighted squeals came as the eels
Entered her sexual quarter.

The ladies of the nation,
Arose in indignation,
They stuffed their bums with chewing gum,
A smart retaliation.

So now we end this serial,
Through sheer lack of material,
I wish you luck and freedom from
Diseases venereal.

The Harlot Of Jerusalem

Tune: London Bridge is Falling Down

In days of old there lived a maid,
She was mistress of her trade,
A prostitute of high repute,
The harlot of Jerusalem.

Chorus:

Hi, ho, Cathusalem,
Cathusalem, Cathusalem,
Hi, ho, Cathusalem,
The harlot of Jerusalem.

And though she fucked for many a year,

Of pregnancy she had no fear,
She washed her passage out with beer,
The best in all Jerusalem.

Now in a hovel by the wall,
A student lived with but one ball,
Who'd been through all, or nearly all,
The harlots of Jerusalem.

His phallic art was lean and tall,
His phallic art caused all to fall,
And victims lined the wailing wall,
That goes around Jerusalem.

One night returning from a spree,
With customary whore-lust he,
Made up his mind to call and see,
The harlot of Jerusalem.

It was for her no fortune good,
That he should need to root his pud,
And choose her out of all the brood,
Of harlots of Jerusalem.

For though he paid his women well,
This syphilitic spawn of hell,
Struck down each year and tolled the bell,
For ten harlots of Jerusalem.

Forth from the town he took the slut,
For 'twas his whim always to rut,
By the Salvation Army hut,
Outside of Old Jerusalem.

With artful eye and leering look,
He took out from its filthy nook,
His penis twisted like a crook,
The Pride of Old Jerusalem.

He leaned the whore against the slum,
And tied her at the knee and bum,
Knowing where the strain would come,
Upon the fair Cathusalem.

He seized the harlot by the bum,
And rattling like a Lewis gun,

He sowed the seed of many a son,
Into the fair Cathusalem.

It was a sight to make you sick,
To hear him grunt so fast and quick,
While rending with his crooked prick,
The womb of fair Cathusalem.

Then up there came an Onanite,
With warty prick besmeared with shite,
He'd sworn that he would goal that night,
The harlot of Jerusalem.

He loathed the art of copulation,
For his delight was masturbation,
And with a spurt of cruel elation,
He saw the whore Cathusalem.

So when he saw the grunting pair,
With roars of rage he rent the air,
And vowed that he would soon take care,
Of the harlot of Jerusalem.

Upon the earth he found a stick,
To which he fastened half a brick,
And took a swipe at the mighty prick,
Of the student of Jerusalem.

He seized the bastard by the crook,
With a burning furious look,
And flung him over Kedrun's Brook,
That babbles past Jerusalem.

The student gave a furious roar,
And rushed to even up the score,
And with his swollen prick did bore,
The cunt of fair Cathusalem.

And reeling full of rage and fight,
He pushed the bastard Onanite,
And rubbed his face in Cathy's shite,
The foulest in Jerusalem.

Cathusalem she knew her part,
She closed her cunt and blew a fart,
That sent him flying like a dart,

Right over Old Jerusalem.

And buzzing like a bumble bee,
He flew straight out towards the sea,
But caught his arsehole in a tree,
That grows in Old Jerusalem.

And to this day you still can see,
His arsehole hanging from that tree,
Let that to you a warning be,
When passing through Jerusalem.

And when the moon is bright and red,
A castrated form sails overhead,
Still raining curses on the head,
Of the harlot of Jerusalem.

As for the student and his lass,
Many a playful night did pass,
Until she joined the VD class,
For harlots of Jerusalem.

The Homer Simpson Drinking Song

Tune: Do-Re-Mi

DOH! A beer! I need a beer!
Ray, the guy who buys me beer!
Me, the guy who Ray buys beer!
Far, the way to go for beer!
So, I think I'll have a beer!
La, la la la la la la...
Tea? No thanks I'll have a beer!
Which brings us back to Doh! doh! doh!

The Irish Rover

In the year of our Lord, eighteen hundred and six
We set sail from the fair Cobh of Cork.
We were bound far away with a cargo of bricks
For the grand city hall of New York.
'Twas a very fine craft, she was rigged fore-and-aft
And oh, how the wild winds drove her.
She had twenty-three masts and withstood several blasts

And we called her the Irish Rover.

There was Barney McGee from the banks of the Lee,
There was Hogan from County Tyrone.
And a chap called McGurk who was scared stiff of work
And a chap from West Meade called Mellone.
There was Slugger O'Toole who was drunk as a rule
And fighting Bill Casey from Dover.
There was Dooley from Claire who was strong as a bear
And was skipper of the Irish Rover.

We had one million bales of old billy goats' tails,
We had two million buckets of stones.
We had three million sides of old blind horses hides,
We had four million packets of bones.
We had five million hogs, six million dogs,
And seven million barrels of porter.
We had eight million bags of the best Sligo rags
In the hold of the Irish Rover.

We had sailed seven years when the measles broke out
And the ship lost her way in a fog.
And the whole of the crew was reduced unto two,
'Twas myself and the captain's old dog.
Then the ship struck a rock with a terrible shock
And then she heeled right over,
Turned nine times around, and the poor dog was drowned
I'm the last of the Irish Rover.

The Live Of The Rover

The old ways are changing, you cannot deny
The day of the traveller's over
There's nowhere to go and there's nowhere to bide
Farewell to the life of the rover.

Chorus:

Farewell to the tent and the old caravan,
To the drinker, the gypsy, the travelling man,
Farewell to the life of the rover.

You've got to live fast to keep up with the times,
These days a man cannot dander,
There's a by-law that says you must be on your way,

Another that says you can't wander.

Farewell to the pony, the cub and the mare
The harness and saddle are idle,
Don't need a trap when you're breaking up scrap,
Farewell to the bit and the bridle.

Repeat first verse and Chorus:

The Limerick Rake

I am a young fellow that's fond of me fun,
In Castletown Conners I'm very well known;
In Newcastle West I spent many a note
With Kitty and Molly and Mary.
My parents rebuked me for being such a rake
And spending my time in such frolicsome ways,
But I ne've could forget the good nature of Jane,
Agus fagaimid siud mar ata se.

My parents, they reared me to shake and to sow,
To plough and to harrow, to reap and to mow;
But my heart was too airy to drop it so low,
I set out on a high speculation.
On paper and parchment they taught me to write
And in Euclid and grammar they opened my eyes,
But in multiplication, in truth, I was bright,
Agus fagaimid siud mar ata se.

To quarrel for riches I ne'er was inclined,
For the greatest of misers must leave them behind;
I'll purchase a cow that will never run dry
And I'll milk her by twisting her horn.
John Damer of Shronel had plenty of gold
And Devonshire's treasure was twenty times more,
But he's laid on his back among nettles and stones,
Agus fagaimid siud mar ata se.

If I chance for to go to the market at Croom,
With a cock in my hat and my pipes in full tune,
I am welcome at once and brought up to a room
Where Bacchus is sporting with Venus.
There's Peggy and Jane from the town of Bruree,
And Biddy from Bruff and we all on the spree,

Such a combing of locks as there was about me,
Agus fagaimid siud mar ata se.

There's some say I'm foolish, there's more say I'm wise,
For love of the women I'm sure 'tis no crime;
For the son of King David had ten hundred wives
And his wisdom is highly recorded.
I'll till a good garden and live at my ease
And the women and children can partake of the same,
If there's war in the cabin, themselves are to blame,
Agus fagaimid siud mar ata se.

And now for the future I mean to be wise,
And I'll send for the women that treated me kind;
And I'll marry them all on the morrow, by and by
If the clergy agree to the bargain.
And when I'm on my back and my soul is at peace
The women will crowd for to cry at my wake,
And their sons and their daughters will utter their prayers
To the Lord for the sake of their father.

The Limerick Song

Tune: (Chorus: only): Cielito Lindo (Mexican Hat Dance: "Aye, aye, aye, aye")

The Chorus: is sung, the limericks spoken.

Chorus:

Aye, aye, aye, aye,
(insert personal insult, such as): Your mother goes down for Egyptians,
So sing me another verse that's worse than the other verse,
And waltz me around by my willie.

More insults:
You mother swims out to meet troop ships
Your mother and father were brothers
Your brother fills empty cream donuts
Your father eats your brother's cream donuts
Your sister eats bat shit off cave walls
Your mother sucks farts from dead seagulls
Your brother beats off in confession
Your mother and sister are brothers
Your sister leaves slime trails like snails

Your mother does squat thrusts on fireplugs
Your family tree has no branches
Your grandmother douches with Drano
Your father sucks farts out of bus seats
Your sister's best friend is a carrot
Your brother just butt-fucked my collie
Your sister goes down for a quarter
Your uncle eats lunch at the sperm bank
Your sister sucks moose cum off pine cones
Your father does eight-year old Brownies
Your mom uses Frisbees for diaphragms
Your sister gives hand jobs to camels
John Deere made your mother's vibrator
Your mother uses hamsters for tampons
Your sister rides bikes without seats
Your mother's so dry the crabs carry canteens
Fuck you and the horse you rode in on!

There once was a young girl named Myrtle,
Who was raped on the beach by a turtle,
The result of the fuck was two eggs and a duck,
Which proved that the turtle was fertile.

There once was a man from Coblenz
Whose ballocks were simply immense
It took 44 laymen
3 priests and a shaman
To carry them hither and hence

A farmer I know named O'Doul
Has a long and remarkable tool
He can use it to plow
Or to diddle a cow
Or just as a cue stick at pool

There once was a man of great class
Whose balls were made out of brass,
When they swung together, they played "Stormy Weather,"
And lighting shot out of his ass.

There once was a man from Rangoon,
Who was born nine months too soon,
He didn't have the luck to be born by a fuck,
He was scraped off the sheets with a spoon.

There once was a man from Kildare,

Who buggered his girl on the stairs,
The bannister broke, so he doubled his stroke,
And finished her off in mid-air.

There was a young man from Dundee,
Who buggered an ape in a tree,
The result was most horrid, all ass and no forehead,
Three balls and a purple goatee.

When a woman in strapless attire,
Found her breasts working higher and higher,
A guest, with great feeling, exclaimed "How appealing!
Do you mind if I piss in the fire?"

There was a young man from Australia,
Who went on a wild bacchanalia,
He buggered a frog, two mice, and a dog,
And a bishop in fullest regalia.

There was a young lady named Anna,
Who stuffed her friend's cunt with banana,
Which she sucked bit by bit, from her partner's warm slit,
In the most approved lesbian manner.

In the Garden of Eden sat Adam,
Just stroking the butt of his madam,
He was quaking with mirth, for on all of the earth,
There were only two balls, and he had 'em.

There was a young lady named Alice,
Who pissed in the Archbishop's chalice,
It was not for the need, she committed the deed,
But simple sectarian malice.

A mathematician named Fine,
Always showed her classes a good time,
Instead of multiplication, she taught fornication,
And never got past sixty-nine.

There was a young lady from Munich,
Who was ravished one night by a eunuch,
At the height of her passion, he slipped her a ration,
From a squirt gun concealed in his tunic.

A woman from South Carolina,
Placed fiddle strings 'cross her vagina,

With proper sized cocks, what was sex, became Bach's
Toccata and Fugue in D Minor.
An unfortunate fellow named Chase,
Had an ass that was badly misplaced,
He showed indignation when an investigation,
Proved that few persons shit through their face.

A certain young maiden from Babylon,
Decided to lure all the rabble on,
By dropping her shirt and raising her skirt,
Exposing a market to dabble-on.

There once was a rabbi from Keith,
Who circumcised men with his teeth.
It was not for the treasure, nor sexual pleasure,
But to get at the cheese underneath.

While Titian was mixing rose madder,
He espied a nude girl on a ladder.
Her position to Titian suggested coition,
So he climed up the ladder and had 'er.

There was a young lady called Annie,
Who had fleas, lice, and crabs up her fanny,
To get up her flue was like touring the zoo,
There were beasties in each nook and cranny.

There was an old whore from the Azores,
Whose cunt was all covered in sores
Even dogs in the street wouldn't touch the green meat,
That hung in festoons from her drawers.

There was a young girl from Assizes,
Whose breasts were of two different sizes,
The left one was small, sweet nothing at all,
The right one was large and won prizes.

There was a young man of Koblenz,
The size of whose balls was immense,
One day playing soccer, he sprung his left knocker,
And kicked it right over the fence.

There was a young lady named Alice,
Who used dynamite for a phallus,
They found her vagina in North Carolina,
Her asshole in Buckingham Palace.

There once was a lady from Arden,
Who sucked a man off in a garden,
He said, "My dear Flo, where does all that stuff go?"
And she said (GULP) "I beg pardon?"
There was a young fellow named Babitt,
Who could screw nine times like a rabbit,
But a girl from Lahore could do it twice more,
Which was just enough extra to crab it.

A lady astrologist in Vancouver,
Once captured a man by maneuver.
Influenced by Venus, she jumped on his penis,
And nothing on Earth could remove her.

There was a young lady of Dexter,
Whose husband exceedingly vexed her,
For whenever they'd start, he'd unfailingly fart
With a blast that damn nearly unsexed her.

There was a young lady from France,
Who decided to take just one chance.
For an hour or so, she just let herself go,
And now all her sisters are aunts.

An Eskimo on his vacation,
Took a night off to succumb to temptation.
'Ere the night was half through, the Eskimo was, too,
For their nights are of six months' duration.

There once was a Duchess of Bruges,
Whose cunt was incredibly huge,
Said the King to his Dame, as he thunderously came,
"Mon Dieu! Apres moi, le deluge!"

Sir Reginald Basington Bart,
Went to a masked ball as a fart,
He had painted his face like a more private place,
And his voice made the dowagers start.

There was a young trucker named Briard,
Who had a young whore that he hired
To fuck when not trucking, but trucking plus fucking
Got him so fucking tired he got fired.

There was a young sailor named Bates,

Who did the fandango on skates,
He fell on his cutlass, which rendered him nutless,
And practically useless on dates.

I once knew a girl named Maureen,
Her cunt was a mass of gangrene,
But health nuts, she found, would still eat her mound,
'Cause maggots are high in protein.

There once was a whore on the dock,
From dusk unti dawn she sucked cock,
Till one day, 'tis said, she gave so much head,
She exploded and whitewashed the dock.

An Argentine gaucho named Bruno,
Said, "Fucking is one thing I do know,
A woman is fine, and sheep are divine,
But a llama is numero uno."

There was a young man from Bengal,
Who had a rectangular ball,
The square of its weight, plus his penis times eight,
Was two-fifths of five-eights of fuck all.
There once was a fellow from Beverly,
Went in for fucking quite heavily,
He fucked night and day till his ballocks gave way,
But the doctors replaced them quite cleverly.

There once was a Bishop of Buckingham,
Who wrote "Assholes and Twelve Ways of Rooting 'em,"
He then went berserk when outdone by a Turk,
Who wrote "Goats and Twelve Ways of Fucking 'em."

When her daughter got married in Bicester,
Her mother remarked as she kissed her,
"That fellow you've won is sure to be fun,
Since tea he's fucked me and your sister."

Then there was the Bishop of Birmingham,
Who diddled the nuns while confirming 'em,
He'd bring them indoors and pull down their drawers,
And slip his Episcopal worm in 'em.

There was a young man of Bombay,
Who fashioned a cunt out of clay,
But the heat of his prick turned the clay into brick,

And it rubbed his foreskin away.

There was a young man of Trieste,
Who loved his young wife with such zest,
Despite all her howls he sucked out her bowels,
And puked up the mess on her chest.

There once was a young man from Boston,
Who traded his car for an Austin,
There was room for his ass and a gallon of gas,
But his balls hung outside and he lost 'em.

There was a young sailor from Brighton,
Who said to his girl, "You're a tight 'un."
She replied, "'Pon my soul, you're in the wrong hole,
There's plenty of room in the right 'un."

There was a young lady named Brent,
With a cunt of enormous extent,
And so deep and wide the acoustics inside
Were so good you could hear when you spent.

There once was a Queen of Bulgaria,
Whose bush had grown hairier and hairier,
Till a Prince from Peru who came for a screw,
Had to hunt for her cunt with a terrier.

There was a young girl who begat,
Triplets called Nat, Pat, and Tat,
It was fun in the breeding, but hell in the feeding,
When she found she had no tit for Tat.

A poofter from old Khartoum,
Lured two lesbians up to his room,
They argued all night over who had the right,
To do what, and with which, and to whom.

A nasty old bugger of Cheltenham,
Once shit in his bags as he knelt in 'em,
He sold them at Ware to a gentleman there,
Who didn't much like what he smelt in 'em.

There once was a man of Cape Nod,
Who attempted to bugger a cod,
When up came some scallops, that nibbled his ballocks,
And now he's a eunuch, by God.

There was a young woman of Chester,
Who said to the man who undressed her,
"I think you will find, that it's better behind,
As the front is beginning to fester."
There was a young woman of Croft,
Who played with herself in the loft,
Having reasoned that candles could never cause scandals,
Besides which they did not go soft.

A policeman from near Clapham Junction,
Had a penis which just wouldn't function,
For the rest of his life he misled his poor wife,
With a snot on the end of his truncheon.

There was a young lady of Cheam
Who crept into the vestry unseen,
She pulled down her knickers, and likewise the vicar's,
And said, "How about it, old bean?"

A pretty young thing from Cape Cod,
Said, "Good things come only from God,"
But 'twas not the Almighty who lifted her nightie,
But Roger, the lodger, the sod.

There was a young man from Killeen,
Who invented a fucking machine,
He pulled out the choke and the bloody thing broke,
And mixed both his balls into cream.

A lady while dining at Crewe,
Found an elephant's dong in her stew,
Said the waiter, "Don't shout, or wave it about,
Or the others will all want one, too."

King Louis, the exemplar of class,
One time was romancing a lass,
When she used the word, "Damn," he rebuked her, "Please ma'am,
Keep a more civil tongue up my ass."

There was an old man of Duluth,
Whose cock was shot off in his youth,
He fucked with his nose, and with fingers and toes,
And he came through a hole in his tooth.

There was a young lady of Kew,
Who said as the Bishop withdrew,

"The Vicar is slicker, and quicker and thicker,
And two inches longer than you."

A habit both vile and unsavory,
Kept the Bishop of London in slavery,
With lecherous howls he deflowered the owls
He kept in an underground aviary.

There was a young couple named Kelly,
Who were found stuck belly to belly,
Because in their haste they used library paste,
Instead of petroleum jelly.

There was a young lady of Trail,
Who offered her body for sale,
She was kind to the blind, for on her behind,
Her prices were written in Braille.

A clever young harlot from Kew,
Filled up her vagina with glue,
She said, with a grin, "If they'll pay to get in,
They can pay to get out of it too."

There was a young fellow from Kent,
Whose tool was most horribly bent,
To save himself trouble he put it in double,
And instead of coming, he went.

There was a young man of Nantucket,
Whose prick was so long he could suck it,
He said with a grin as he wiped off his chin,
"If my ear were I cunt, I'd fuck it."

A man on a farm in Moritz,
Once planted two acres of titz,
They came up in the fall, pink nipples and all,
Then he leisurely chewed them to bitz.

To his bride said the one-eyed detective,
"Can it be that my eyesight's defective?
Has your east tit the least bit, the best of your west tit,
Or is it a trick of perspective?"

A hillbilly farmer named Hollis,
With possums and snakes sought his solace.
His children had scales and prehensile tails,

And voted for Governor Wallace.
There once was a man from Newcastle,
Who had a collapsible asshole.
It was handy, you see, when he farted at sea,
He could bend down and make up a parcel.

There was a young man from Devizes,
Whose ballocks were two different sizes.
One weighed a full pound and dragged on the ground,
The other was large as a fly's is.

An insatiable nymph from Penzance,
Traveled by train to South France.
Five others fucked her besides the conductor,
And the engineer came in his pants.

A lady who lived in South Mimms,
Had the most overwhelming of quims.
The priest of the diocese has elephantiasis,
So it wasn't all singing and hymns.

There was a young fellow from Nottingham,
Who saved up tin cans and put snot in 'em.
He threw in some shit to spice it a bit,
And sold 'em to boys, who shot off in 'em.

There was a young girl from Bahia,
Who liked sticking flutes up her rea-ha.
After eating escargots she could fart Handel's "Largo,"
Her encore was "Ave Maria."

There was a young fellow from Stroud,
Who could fart unbelievably loud.
When he let go a big 'un, dogs were deafened in Wigan,
And the windowpanes shattered in Oudh.

There once was a sheik from Algiers,
Who said to his harem, "My dears,
You may think it odd of me, but I've given up sodomy,
And taken up fucking." Three cheers!

A randy young buck of Lahore,
Was asked when he rogered his whore.
He said "At eleven, at three, five, and seven,
And eight, and a quarter past four."

There once was an monk from Siberia,
Who seemed to get wearier and wearier.
No wonder; this monk was sharing his bunk
Each night with the Mother Superior.

There was a young lady named Hilda,
Who went for a walk with a builder.
He knew that he could, and he should, and he would,
And he did, and he goddamn near killed her.

A chap down in old Oklahoma,
Had a cock that could sing "La Paloma."
But the sweetness of pitch couldn't put off the hitch,
Of impotence, size, and aroma.

A disgusting young lad named McGill,
Made his neighbors exceedingly ill
When they learned of his habits involving white rabbits,
And a bird with a flexible bill.

There was a young girl named McCall,
Whose cunt was exceedingly small.
But the size of her anus was something quite heinous,
It could hold seven pricks and one ball.

A broken down harlot named Tupps,
Was heard to confess over cups,
"The height of my folly was fucking a collie,
But I got a nice price for the pups."

The handsome young plumber McGee,
Was plumbing a girl by the sea.
She said, "Stop your plumbing, there's somebody coming!"
Said the plumber, still plumbing, "It's me."

There was a young parson named Bings,
Who talked about women and things.
But his secret desire was a boy in the choir,
With a bottom like jelly on springs.

An elderly pervert in Nice,
Was long past wanting a piece.
He jacked off his hogs, his cow, and his dogs,
Till his parrot called in the police.

There was a young girl of Devon,

Who was raped in the garden by seven
High Anglican priests, the lascivious beasts,
Of such is the Kingdom of Heaven.

The last time I dined with the King,
He did a curious thing.
He stood on a stool and took out his tool,
And said, "If I play, will you sing?"

There was a young lady from Natchez,
Who happened to be born with two snatches.
She said, with some wit, "I'd give either tit,
For a man with equipment that matches."

There once was a lady from Wheeling,
Who claimed she lacked sexual feeling.
Till a fellah named Boris touched her clitoris,
And they scraped her off of the ceiling.

There once was a man named McSweeney,
Who once spilled some gin on his weenie.
Now, just to be couth, he added vermouth,
And slipped his girl a martini.

We recall with the fondest of ease
The front aperture of Louise.
Tho' shaped like a funnel, 'twas large as a tunnel
With a space for a flying trapeze.

There was a young lady at sea,
Who complained that it hurt her to pee.
Said the brawny old mate, "That accounts for the state,
Of the cook and the captain and me."

An inventor of genius named Moore,
Made himself a mechanical whore.
But he failed when he wooed her, she unscrewed as he screwed her,
And her clit clattered down to the floor.

A self-centered sugar named Perkins,
Would work off her urges with gherkins.
Until, with a skid, inside her one slid,
And pickled her internal workin's.

One evening a guru had coitus,
With an actress, a whore and a poetess.

When asked what position he used for coition,
He answered serenely, "The lotus."

Cried an overhung fellow named Bowen,
"My pecker keeps growin' and growin'.
It's got so tremendulous, so long and so pendulous,
It's no good for pecking . . . just showin'!"

There once was a fellow named Potts,
Who was prone to having the trots.
But his humble abode was without a commode,
So his carpet was covered with spots.

A pretty young lady named Vogel,
Once sat herself down on a molehill.
A curious mole nosed into her hole--
Ms. Vogel's okay, but the mole's ill.

There was a young man named Crockett,
Whose balls got caught in a socket.
His wife--what a bitch--threw the switch,
As Crockett went off like a rocket.

On a cannibal isle near Malaysia,
Lives a lady they call Anastasia.
Not Russian elite--she's eager to eat
Whatever or whoever lays her.

There was a young girl from Hong Kong
Whose cervical cap was a gong.
She said with a yell, as a shot rang her bell,
"I'll give you a ding for a dong!"

There once was a man named Howells,
Who sucked shit from other mens' bowels.
He also did this with prostitutes' piss,
And the drippings from sanitary towels!

A nervous old codger named Royce
Couldn't control his sphincter by choice.
So he speedily strode to his favorite commode,
Blew his nose, blew his ass, and rejoiced.
There once was a man from Los Leaver
Who had an affair with a beaver.
The results of that fuck were a canvas-backed duck,
Two canoes, and a golden retriever.

A languid young man from Racine
Wasn't weaned until nearly sixteen.
He said, "I'll admit there's no milk in the tit,
But think of the fun it has been."

There was a young fellow from Sparta
Who was the world's champion farter,
On the strength of one bean he'd fart God Save the Queen,
And Beethoven's Moonlight Sonata.

He could vary, with proper persuasion,
His fart to suit any occasion.
He could fart like a flute, like a lark, like a lute,
This highly fartistic Caucasian.

He'd fart a gavotte for a starter,
And fizzle a fine serenata.
He could play on his anus the Coriolanus:
Oof, boom, er-tum, tootle, hum tah-dah!

He was great in the Christmas Cantata,
He could double-stop fart The Toccata,
He'd boom from his ass Bach's B-Minor Mass,
And in counterpoint, La Traviata.

Spurred on by a very high wager
With an envious Sergeant Major,
He proceeded to fart the complete oboe part
Of the Hayden Octet in B-Major.

It went off in capital style,
And he farted it through with a smile;
Then, feeling quite jolly, he tried the finale
Blowing double-stopped farts all the while.

The selection was tough, I admit,
But it did not dismay him one bit,
'Til with ass thrown aloft he suddenly coughed --
And collapsed in a shower of shit!

The Lumberjack Song

I'm a lumberjack and I'm O.K.,
I sleep all night and I work all day.

He's a lumberjack, and he's O.K.
He sleeps all night and he works all day.

I cut down trees, I eat my lunch
I go to the lavatory.
On Wednesdays I go shopping
And have buttered scones for tea.
He cuts down trees, he eats his lunch
He goes to the lavatory.
On Wednesdays he goes shopping
And has buttered scones for tea.
He's a lumberjack, and he's O.K.
He sleeps all night and he works all day.

I cut down trees, I skip and jump
I like to press wild flowers
I put on women's clothing
And hang around in bars.
He cuts down trees, he skips and jumps
He likes to press wild flowers
He puts on women's clothing
And hangs around in bars?
He's a lumberjack, and he's O.K.
He sleeps all night and he works all day.

I cut down trees, I wear high heels
Suspendies and a bra
I wish I'd been a girlie
Just like my dear pappa.
He cuts down trees, he wear high heels?
Suspendies...and a bra?
...He's a lumberjack, and he's O.K.
He sleeps all night and he works all day.

The Mooth Hymn Of The Republic

Mine eyes have seen the sorrow of the morning intel brief,
A tale of woe and suffering and tragic human grief;
So now we're doing NEO and delivering relief!
It's war--no, it's not! What the Hell??

Chorus:

Glory, glory, mobilization!
Time to save another nation!

Bring relief to Kurds and Hatians!
It's war--no, it's not! What the Hell?

The general says it's time to pack our A-Bags once again,
get ready for the mission, doesn't matter where or when;
but we know that the boss gets his commands from CNN!
It's war--no, it's not! What the Hell??

The Aviano flyers waste their time and waste their skills
drilling circles in the sky and bombing empty hills;
O'Grady got a book deal, but the rest of us got nil!
It's war--no, it's not! What the hell?

Somalia exploded and the news reporters said,
"You've got to feed the hungry, there's enough already dead."
But now we're under fire from the people that we fed!
It's war--no, it's not! What the Hell??

Then came the fateful order to get ready for Zaire,
Another JTF to further somebody's career.
It's so bad CNN sent Christiana Amanpour!
It's war--no, it's not! What the Hell??

Civilians give us shit and cut our budget to the bone;
they treat us like we're lepers or official Al Capones--
until they need some press, or need another No-Fly Zone!
It's war--no, it's not! What the Hell??

We used to guard the world from Soviets and Red Chinese,
we've battled Cubans, North Koreans, and Vietnamese;
but now we're fit for nothing more than feeding refugees!
It's war--no, it's not! What the Hell??

The Mouse Song

The liquor was spilt on the barroom floor,
And the bar was closed for the night,
When out of his hole came a little brown mouse,
And he sat in the pale moonlight.

He lapped up the liquor on the barroom floor,
And on his haunches he sat,
And all night long you could hear him roar,
"BRING ON YER GODDAM CAT! HIC! *CAT!* HIC! *CAT!"*

The Old Department Store

Tune: The Bear Went Over the Mountain

Chorus:

> *I used to work in Chicago*
> *In the old department store.*
> *I used to work in Chicago,*
> *I don't work there anymore.*

A woman came in for a hammer,
A hammer from the store?
A hammer she wanted, nailed she got,
I don't work there anymore.

More verses:
Some nails... screwed
Some paper... a ream
A screen door… the back door she got
Some meat… my sausage she got
A hammer… banged she got
A carpet… shagged she got
Fishing wire… my rod she got
Some beef… porked she got
A Camel… humped she got
A helicopter… my chopper she got
An elevator... my shaft she got
A KitKat… four fingers she got
Some wool... felt she got
Some rubber nipples... rub her nipples I did
Some whiskey she wanted... liquor I did
Some floppy disks... a hard drive she got
Some china... my bone she got
Some stockings... a hosing she got
Some Drano... clean pipes she got
Some tires... rimmed she got
Glazed donut she wanted... cream-filled she got
A watchspring she wanted... boinged she got
A T-bone she wanted... boneless round she got
Some toy sailors she wanted... semen she got
A Dickens novel... my Longfellow she got
Some lobster... crabs she got
Some film... exposed she got
A lady came in for a video... Free Willy she wanted, free willie I did
Fuck she wanted, fuck she got!

The Old Dun Cow

Some friends and I in a public house
Were playing dominoes one night,
When in through the door a fireman rushed,
His face all chalky white.
"What's up?" says Brown, "Have you seen a ghost?
Have you seen your Aunt Moriah?"
"Me Aunt Moriah be buggered!" says he,
"The bleedin' pub's on fire!"

"On fire!" says Brown, "What a bit of luck!
Everybody follow me;
We'll go to the cellar, if the fire's not there,
We'll have a grand old spree.
So we all went down with good ol' Brown,
And the liquor we could not miss,
And we weren't there ten minutes more
When we were all quite pissed.

Chorus: Oh, there was Brown (WHERE?), Upside-down,
Mopping up the whiskey on the floor,
"BOOZE! BOOZE!" the firemen cried,
As they came knocking on the door. KNOCK-KNOCK-KNOCK
Oh, don't let 'em in 'till it's all mopped up,
Somebody shouted "MacKintyre" MACKINTYRE!
And we all got blue blind paralytic drunk when the Old Dun Cow caught fire.

Now Tom ran over to the port wine tub,
And gave it a few hard knocks,
He started taking off his pantaloons,
Likewise his shoes and socks.
"Now look," says Brown, "If you want to wash yer feet,
Now let's get one thing clear,
You don't put your trotters in the port wine tub
When we've got some old stale beer."

Then all of a sudden there was such a bloody crash,
Half the bleedin' roof gave way,
We were soaked in the fireman's hose,
But still we felt quite gay.
We got some sacks and some old tin tacks,
And we pinned ourselves inside.
And we all got drinking fine old ale,
Until we were bleary eyed.

The Penis Song (The Not Noel Coward Song)

(spoken) Good evening, ladies and gentlemen.
Here's a little number I tossed off recently in the Caribbean.

Isn't it awfully nice to have a penis,
Isn't it frightfully good to have a dong?
It's swell to have a stiffy,
It's divine to own a dick,
From the tiniest little tadger,
To the world's biggest prick.
So three cheers for you willy or John Thomas,
Hooray for your one-eyed trouser snake,
Your piece of pork, Your wife's best friend,
Your percy or your cock,
You can wrap it up in ribbons,
You can slip it in your sock,
But don't take it out in public,
Or they will stick you in the dock,
And you won't come back.

(spoken) Thank you very much, yes, indeed.

The Pilosophers Song

Monty Python

Immanual Kant was a real pissant who was very rarely stable
Heidegger, Heidegger was a boozy beggar who could think you under the table
David Hume could out-consume Schopenhauer and Hegel
And Wittgenstein was a beery swine who was just as shloshed as Schlegel

There's nothing Nietzche couldn't teach ya 'bout the raising of the wrist
Socrates himself was permanently pissed

John Stuart Mill of his own free will on half a pint of shandy was particularly ill
Plato they say could stick it away, half a crate of whiskey every day
Aristotle, Aristotle was a bugger for the bottle, Hobbes was fond of his dram
And Rene' Descartes was a drunken fart, "I drink, therefore I am"

Yes, Socrates himself is particularly missed,
A lovely little thinker, but a bugger when he's pissed.

The Pioneers

Tune: Son of a Gambolier

The pioneers have hairy ears,
They piss through leather britches,
They wipe their ass with broken glass,
Those tough old sons of bitches.

When cunt is rare, they fuck a bear,
They knife him if he snitches,
They knock their cocks against the rocks,
Those hardy sons of bitches.

They take their ass upon the grass,
In bushes or in ditches,
Their two-pound dinks are full of kinks,
Those rough-hewn sons of bitches.

Without remorse, they fuck a horse,
And beat him if he twitches,
Their two-foot pricks are full of nicks,
Those mean old sons of bitches.

To make a mule stand for the tool,
They beat him with hickory switches,
They use their pricks for walking sticks,
Those gnarled old sons of bitches.

Great joy they reap from cornholing sheep,
In barns, or bogs, or ditches,
Nor give a damn if it be a ram,
Those grimy sons of bitches.

They walk around, prick to the ground,
And kick it if it itches,
And if it throbs, they scratch it with cobs,
Those mighty sons of bitches.

The Poetry Song

Tune: Chorus: from The Little Brown Jug

This is performed in the same manner as the Limericks, with spoken verses and singing Chorus:, verses alternating around the circle

Chorus:

> *Poerty, poetry,*
> *How do you like my poerty?*
> *Not as mellow as Longfellow,*
> *But it's poetry.*

Mary had a little lamb,
Its fleece was white as snow.
And everywhere that Mary went,
The lamb was sure to go.
It followed her to school one day, school one day, school one day,
It followed her to school one day,
And a big black dog fucked it!

Mary had a little sheep,
And with the sheep she went to sleep,
The sheep turned out to be a ram,
And Mary had a little lamb.

When Mary had a little lamb,
The doctor was surprised.
But when Old MacDonald had a farm,
The doctor nearly died.

Mary had a little lamb,
Its fleece was white as snow.
And everywhere that Mary went,
The lamb was sure to go.
The price of meat arose too high,
Which really didn't please her.

Tonight she's having leg of lamb,
The rest is in the freezer.
Mary had a little lamb,
She tied it to a pylon.
10,000 volts went up its ass,
And turned its wool to nylon.

Mary had a little lamb,
She kept in her yard.

Every time she took her panties off,
His little wooly dick got hard.

Mary had a little lamb,
The doctors were astounded.
Everywhere that Mary went,
Gynecologists surrounded.

Mary had a little lamb,
She couldn't stop it crying;
So she kicked it in the ass one day,
And sent it fucking flying.

Mary had a little lamb,
Forever it was gluing.
Making models of its friends,
In strange positions, screwing.

Mary had a little lamb,
With carrots and with peas.
A little mint sauce on the top,
And stuffing in its knees.

Mary had a little lamb,
She liked to stroke its head.
Until one day she found her husband
Fucking it in her bed.

Mary had a little lamb,
Its fleece was white as snow.
And everywhere that Mary went,
The lamb didn't, because Mary was cunt.

Mary had a little lamb,
A giraffe and zebra too,
By the time she'd finished,
She'd fucked the whole damn zoo.

Mary had a little lamb
And now I've had enough
Of this stupid girl called Mary
And her wooly bit of muff.

Little Jack Horner
Sat in the corner,
Fingering his sister Mary.

He stuck in his thumb,
And pulled out a plum,
And said, "Ain't it supposed to be a cherry?"

Little Miss Muffet,
Sat on a tuffet,
Eating her curds and whey.
Along came a spider,
Who sat down beside her,
And said, "Yo, what's in the bowl, bitch?"

Old Mother Hubbard
Went to the cupboard,
To get her poor dog a bone.
But when old Mother bent over,
Rover he drove her, 'cause
He had a bone of his own.

Old Mother Hubbard
Went to the cupboard,
To get her poor daughter a dress.
When she got there the cupboard was bare,
And so was her daughter, I guess.

There once was an old lady,
Who lived in a shoe,
She had so many kids that her
Cunt could stretch over a trash can.

Jack and Jill went up the hill,
To fetch a pail of water,
Jill came down with half a crown,
But not for fetching water.

Jack and Jill went up the hill,
On an elephant.
Jill got down and helped
Jack off the elephant.

Jack and Jill went up the hill,
For just an itty bitty.
Jill's now two months overdue,
And Jack has left the city.

Jack and Jill went up the hill,
To fetch a pail of water.

Silly Jill forgot the pill,
And now they have a daughter.

Jack and Jill went up the hill,
To have a little fun.
Stupid Jill! Forgot that pill!
So now they have a son.

Jack and Jill went up the hill,
With a keg of brandy.
Jack got stewed, Jill got screwed,
Now it's Jack, Jill and Andy

Jack and Jill went up the hill,
To smoke a little leaf.
Jack got high, pulled down his fly,
And Jill said, "Where's the beef!"

Jack and Jill went up the hill,
And planned to do some kissing.
Jack made a pass, and grabbed her ass
And now two of his front teeth are missing.

Jack and Jill went up the hill,
Both carrying a bucket.
When Jill bent down, her ass was round,
And Jack decided to fuck it.

Jack and Jill went up the hill,
For a bit of hanky panky.
Jill came back with a very sore crack,
Jack must have been a Yankee

Jack and Jill went up the hill,
Each with a buck and a quarter.
Jill came down with two-fifty,
The fuckin' whore!

Humpty Dumpty sat on a wall,
Humpty Dumpty had a great fall,
All the king's horses, and all the king's men,
Had one fucking big omelette.

Jack be nimble, Jack be quick,
Jack jumped over the candlestick,
Jack be nimble, Jack be quick,

Jackie burned off his fucking dick.

Jack was nimble, Jack was quick,
But Jill preferred the candlestick!

Little Willie, full of glee,
Put radium in grandma's tea.
Now he thinks it quite a lark,
To see her shining in the dark.

Little Willie, brand new skates.
Hole in ice, pearly gates.

The birds may kiss the bees goodbye,
The buttercup, the butterfly.
The morning dew may kiss the grass,
And you, my friend, may kiss my ass.

Oh give me a home,
Where the buffalo roam,
Where the deer and the antelope play.
Where seldom is heard,
A discouraging word,
'Cause deer and antelope can't fucking talk!

Rub-a-dub dub, three men in a tub…
Butt-fucking!

Roses are red,
Violets are for plucking.
Girls out of high school,
Are ready for college.

The Pub With No Beer

It's lonesome away from your kindred and all
By the camp fire at night where the wild dingoes call,
But there's nothing so lonesome so morbid or drear
Than to stand in a bar of a pub with no beer.
Now the publican's anxious for the quota to come
There's a far away lock on the face of the bum
The maid's gone all cranky and the cook's acting queer
What a terrible place is a pub with no beer.

Then the stock-man rides up with his dry dusty throat
He breasts up to the bar, pulls a wat from his coat,
But the smile on his face quickly turns to a sneer,
When the bar man said sadly the pub's got no beer.

Ther's a dog on the 'randa-h for his master he waits
But the boss is inside drinking wine with his mates
He hurries for cover and cringes in fear
It's no place for a dog round a pub with no beer.

Old Billy the blacksmith first time in his life
Has gone home cold sober to his darling wife,
He walks in the kitchen, she says you're early me dear,
But he breaks down and tells her the pub's got no beer.

The Pushin' Song

Was it you who did the pushin'
Left the stains upon the cushion
Footprints on the dashboard upside-down
(Oh upside-down!)
Was it you, you sly woodpeckah
Got inside my girl Rebecca
If it was, you better leave this town!

(The reply): It was I that did the pushin'
Left the stains upon the cushion
Footprints on the dashboard upside-down
(Oh upside-down!)
Ever since I had your daughter
I've had trouble passing water
Guess we'll call it evens all around.

The Recruiting Sergeant

As I was walking down the road
Feeling fine and larky oh
A recruiting Sergeant came up to me
Says he you'd look fine in khaki oh
For the King he is in need of men
Come read this proclamation oh
A life in Flanders for you then
Would be a fine vacation now.

That may be so says I to him
But tell me sergent Dearie-oh
If I had a pack stuck upon me back
Would I look fine and cheerie oh
For they'd have you train and drill until
They had you one of Frenchies oh
It maybe warm in Flanders
But it's draughty in the trenches oh.

The Sergeant smiled and winked his eye
His smile was most provoking oh
He twiddled and twirled his wee moustache
Says he I know your only joking oh
For the sandbags are so warm and high
The wind you won't feel blowing oh
Well I winked at a colleen passing by
Says I what if it's snowing oh.

Come rain or hail or wind or snow
I'm not going out to Flanders oh
There's fighting in Dublin to be done
Let your Sergeants and Commanders go
Let Englishmen fight English wars
It's nearly time they started oh
I salute the Sergeant a very good night
And there and then we parted oh.

The Restroom Door Said "Gentlemen"

Tune: God Rest Ye Merry Gentlemen

The restroom door said "Gentlemen" so I just walked inside,
I took two steps and realized I'd been taken for a ride.
I heard high voices, turned and found the place was occupied
By three nuns, two old ladies and a nurse.
What could be worse,
Than three nuns, two old ladies and a nurse?

The restroom door said "Gentlemen," it must have been a gag.
As soon as I did walk therein, I bumped on some old hag.
She sprayed me with a can of Mace and hit me with her bag.
It just wasn't cut out to be my day.
What can I say?
It just wasn't cut out to be my day!

The restroom door said "Gentlemen" and I would like to find,
The crummy little creep who had the nerve to switch the sign.
'Cause I've got two black eyes and one high heel up my behind.
Never more will I sit in comfort or joy.
Boy oh boy!
Never more will I sit in comfort or joy.

The Ring-Dang-Doo

Chorus:

The ring-dang-doo, pray what is that?
It's furry and soft, like a pussycat,
It's got a crack down the middle,
And a hole right through,
That's what they call the ringadangdoo.

I once knew a girl, her name was Jean,
The sweetest girl I'd ever seen,
She loved a boy who was straight and true,
Who longed to play on her ring-dang-doo.

So she took him to her father's house,
And crept inside as quiet as a mouse,
And they shut the door and the window too,
And he played all night on her ring-dang-doo.

The very next day her father said,
"You've gone and lost your maidenhead!
You can pack your bag and suitcase too,
And bugger off with your ring-dang-doo."

So she went to town and became a whore,
And hung a red light outside her door,
And one by one and two by two,
They came to play on her ring-dang-doo.

There came to that town a son of a bitch,
Who had the pox and the seven-year itch,
He had gonorrhea and syphilis too
So that was the end of her ring-dang-doo.

The Sexual Life Of A Camel

The sexual life of the camel,
Is stranger than anyone thinks,
At the height of the mating season
He tries to bugger the Sphinx.
But the Sphinx's posterior sphincter
Is clogged by the sands of the Nile,
Which accounts for the hump on the camel,
And the Sphinx's inscrutable smile.

Chorus:

Singing, bum-titty, bum-titty, titty-bum,
Bum-titty, bum-titty, aye.
Singing, bum-titty, bum-titty, titty-bum,
Bum-titty, bum-titty, aye.

In the process of civilization,
From the anthropoid ape down to man,
It is generally held that the Navy
Has buggered whatever it can,
Yet recent extensive researches
By Darwin and Huxley and Hall,
Conclusively prove that the hedgehog
Has never been buggered at all.

We therefore believe our conclusion
Is incontrovertibly shown,
That comparative safety on shipboard
Is enjoyed by the hedgehog alone.
Why haven't they done it at Spithead,
As they've done it at Harvard and Yale,
And also at Oxford and Cambridge,
By shaving the spines off its tail?

It was Christmas Eve in the harem,
The eunuchs were all standing there,
While dozens of dusky young maidens,
Sat combing their pubic hair.
And then came along Father Christmas,
Striding down the marble halls,
When he asked what they wanted for Christmas,
The eunuchs all answered, "Our balls!"

The Scotsman

A Scotsman clad in kilt left the bar one evening fair,
And one could see by how he walked that he'd drunk more than his share,
He wandered on until he could no longer keep his feet,
Then he stumbled off into the grass to sleep beside the street.

Ring dem diddle iddle aye, hey,
Ring dem diddley aye oh,
He stumbled off into the grass to sleep beside the street.

Now about that time two young and lovely lassies wandered by,
And one says to the other with a twinkle in her eye,
"See yon sleeping Scotsman, so strong and handsome built,
I wonder if it's true what they don't wear beneath their kilt?"

Ring dem diddle iddle aye, hey,
Ring dem diddley aye oh,
I wonder if it's true what they don't wear beneath their kilt?

So they crept up on the sleeping Scotsman quiet as could be,
Then lifted up his kilt about a yard so they could see,
And lo, behold for them to view beneath his Scottish skirt,
There was nothing more than God had graced him with upon his birth.

Ring dem diddle iddle aye, hey,
Ring dem diddley aye oh,
There was nothing more than God had graced him with upon his birth.

So they marveled for a moment, then one said "We'd best be gone,
But let's leave a something before we move along."
As a gift they left a blue silk ribbon tied into a bow,
Around the bonnie spar the Scotman's kilt did lifted show.

Ring dem diddle iddle aye, hey,
Ring dem diddley aye oh,
Around the bonnie spar the Scotman's kilt did lifted show.

So the Scotsman woke to nature's call and stumbled for the trees,
Behind a bush, he lifts his kilt and gawks at what he sees,
Then in a startled voice he says to what's before his eyes,
"Oh lad, I don't know where you've been, but I see you won first prize!"

Ring dem diddle iddle aye, hey,

Ring dem diddley aye oh,
"Lad I don't know where you've been, but I see you won first prize."

The Scottish Wedding Song

Tune: The Ball of Kirriemuir

'Twas on the first of August the party, it began.
Now, never shall I forget, me lads, the gatherin' of the clans.

Chorus:

Singing, "Balls to your partner, ass against the wall.
If you can't get laid on a Saturday night, you'll never get laid at all."

Four and twenty virgins came down from Inverness,
and when the ball was over there were four and twenty less.

'Twas the ball of Kirriemuir, me lads, and everyone was there
A-playin' with the lassies an' twinin' curly hair.

The bride was in the bedroom, explainin' to the groom
The vagina, not the rectum, is the entrance to the womb.

The groom was in the bedroom, explainin' to the bride,
The penis, not the scrotum, is the part that goes inside.

Four and twenty prostitutes came up from Glockamore,
And when the ball was over they were all of them double bore.

There was fuckin' in the meadows, there was fuckin' in the ricks,
You couldn't hear the bagpipes for the pounding of the pricks.

Mr. MacFudge the parson, he went among the women,
He took poor Nellie on his knee, and filled her full o' semen.

Poor wee Nellie she found out, to her great consternation,
By some strange means or other, she increased his congregation.

The parson's daughter, she was there, a sittin' way down front
A wreath of roses in her hair and a carrot up her cunt.
The parson's wife, she was there, her arse against the wall,
Shoutin' to the laddie boys, "I'll take ye one an' all."

The minister's scivvy, she was there, she was all dressed in blue,
They tied her to the barn door, an' bulled her like a coo.

It's the first lady forward, and the second lady back
And the third lady's finger in the fourth lady's crack.

The village pervert, he was there, and on the floor he sat
Amusing himself by abusing himself and catching it on his hat.

The undertaker came to call, dressed in a lime black shroud
Swinging on the chandelier and pissing on the crowd.

The mayor's daughter, she was there, and kept the crowd in fits
By jumpin' off the mantle piece and landin' on her tits.

They were banging on the bannister, screwing on the stairs
Ye couldn't see the carpet for the mess o' pubic hairs.

The village idiot, he was there, he was a perfect fool.
He sat beneath the oak tree and whittled off his tool.

The village postman, he was there, the poor man had the pox
No lassie would go near him, so he fucked the letter box.

The chimney sweeper, he was there, we had to put him out,
For every time he farted, he filled the room with soot.

The groom by now was excited an' racin' through the halls
He was pullin' on his pecker an' showin off his balls.

The doctor's wife, oh, she was there, she wasn't very weel,
For she had to make her water, in the midst of ev'ry reel.

The butcher's wife, oh, she was there, she also wasn't weel,
For she had to go and piddle, after ev'ry little feel.

There was fuckin' in the courtyard, fuckin' in the halls,
You couldn't hear the music, for the janglin' of the balls.

They was bangin' on the bannister, screwing on the stairs,
And when the railing broke, they were mating in mid-air.

The minister's daughter she was there, all draped up to the front,
With roses round her cute wee arse, but thistles up her cunt.

Four an' twenty dairymaids, lyin' out all bare,
You couldn't see the daisies, for the cunts an' curly hair.

The farmer's son, oh, he was there, an' he was in the byre,

Introducin' masturbation, with an Indian rubber tire.

The village bobby he was here, he'd put on fancy socks,
He fucked a lassie forty times, an' found she had the pox.

The auld schoolteacher she was there, she didn't bring her stick,
She wasn't much to look at, but she sure could take the prick.

The village cripple he was there, he wasn't up to much,
He lined 'em up against the wall and shagged 'em with his crutch.

The King was in the counting house, a-countin' out his wealth,
The Queen was in the parlour, a-diddlin' with herself.

The Queen was in the parlour, a-eating bread and honey,
The King was in the chambermaid, an' she was in the money.

The King's magician, he was there, playing his favourite trick,
He pulled his foreskin over his head, and vanished up his prick.

The barrister's daughter she was there, the cunning little runt,
With poison ivy up her bum, and thistle up her cunt.

The village plumber he was there, he felt an awful fool,
He'd come eleven leagues or more and forgot to bring his tool.

The village doctor he was there, sitting by the fire,
Doing abortions by the score with a piece of red hot wire.

And in between abortions, he had his bag of tricks,
And in between the dances he was sterilizing pricks.

There was fucking in the barley, fucking in the oats,
Some were fucking sheep and some were fucking goats.

The village trader, he was there, his pecker in his hand,
Waiting for the moment when supply would meet demand.
The village blacksmith he was there, his balls were made of brass,
And ev'ry time he tried to fuck, sparks flew out of his ass.

The blacksmith's brother he was there, a mighty man was he,
He lined them up against the wall and buggered them three by three.

The blacksmith's father he was there, a-roaring like a lion,
He'd cut his rod off in the forge, so he used a red-hot iron.

The blacksmith's son he was there, acting quite the fool,
Pulling his foreskin over his head and whistling through his tool.

The village hooker she was there, laying on the floor,
And every time she spread her legs, the suction closed the door.

Expectant ladies, they were there, having lots of fun,
And every time you ate one out, a hand would grab your tongue.

Little granny, she was there, sitting by the fire,
Knitting prophylactics out of BF Goodrich tires.

Farmer Giles he was there, his sickle in his hand,
And every time he swung around he circumcised the band.

Farmer Johnson, he was there, an' he just cursed an' spat
For forty acres of his oats were fucked completely flat.

The village builder he was there, he brought his bag of tricks,
He poured cement in all the holes, and blunted all the pricks.

Now little Tommy he was there, but he was only eight,
He couldna root the women, so he had to masturbate.

The parson's wife was yet still there, swinging on the chandelier
Spreading menstrual juices into everybody's beer.

An' when the ball was over, the ladies all confessed,
They'd all enjoyed the dancin', but the fuckin' was the best.

MANDATORY LAST VERSE:
The beaming father of the bride was quite surprised to see
Four and twenty maidenheads a-hangin' from the tree.

The S&M Man

Tune: The Candy Man

Who takes jumper cables,
Attaches 'em to her tits,
Connects them to a Mack truck and has orgasmic fits?

Chorus:

The S&M Man,
The S&M Man

The S&M Man, 'cause he mixes it with love,
And makes the hurt feel good (the hurt feel good).

Who can take two ice-picks
shove 'em in her ears
Ride her like a Harley while he fucks her in the rear?
The S&M Man...

Who can take a bicycle
Rip off the seat
Put on his grandma, and shove her down a bumpy street?
The S&M Man...

Who sleeps on barbed wire,
Tossing left and right,
Just to see how many stitches he can earn each night?
The S&M Man...

Who rubs down with honey,
Just to have a chance
To lay out on the lawn and be a picnic for the ants?
The S&M Man...

Who ties down his sweetie,
Each and every day,
Covers her with rats and lets the kitties in to play?
The S&M Man...

Who can take a razor,
And no shaving cream,
Scrape her pussy bald while he listens to her scream?
The S&M Man...

Who can take a bottle,
Shove it up your ass,
Hit it with a hammer, and line your ass with glass?
The S&M Man...

Who can take your scrotum,
Stick it with a pin,
Hang a bunch of weights until it hangs down to your shins?
The S&M Man...

Who could take a condom,
Put pepper in the ring,
Use it on the girl, because she twitches when it stings?

The S&M Man...

Who can take a pregnant woman,
Lay her on the bed,
Fuck her in the pussy while the fetus gives him head,
The S&M Man...

Who can take a vice clamp,
Tight upon a tit,
Squeeze the sucker down until it pops just like a zit?
The S&M man...

Who can take a cheese grater,
Strap it to his arm,
Fist fuck the bitch, and make Vagina Parmesan?
The S&M Man...

Who can take a baby,
Lay it on a bed,
Turn the bugger over, fuck the soft spot in its head?
The S&M Man...

Who can go to an abortion clinic,
Sneak around the back,
Root through all the dumpsters looking for a tasty snack?

The Wild Colonial Boy

There was a wild colonial boy, Jack Duggan was his name
He was born and bred in Ireland in a place called Castlemaine
He was his father's only son, his mother's pride and joy
And dearly did his parents love the Wild Colonial Boy
At the age of sixteen years he left his native home
And through Australia's sunny clime he was inclined to roam
He robbed the lordly squatters, their flocks he would destroy
A terror to Australia was the Wild Colonial Boy

For two long years this darling youth ran on his wild career
With a heart that knew no danger, and of justice did not fear
He stuck the Beechworth coach up and he robbed judge McEvoy
Who, trembling gave his gold up to the Wild Colonial Boy

He bade the judge "good morning" and he told him to beware
For he never robbed an honest judge what acted on the square

Yet you would rob a mother of her son and only joy
And breed a race of outlaws like the Wild Colonial Boy

One morning on the prairie Wild Jack Duggan rode along
While listening to the mocking birds singing a cheerful song
Out jumped three troopers fierce and grim, Kelly, Davis and Fitzroy
They all set out to capture him, the Wild Colonial Boy

He fired point blank at Kelly and brought him to the ground
He fired a shot at Davis too, who fell dead at the sound
But a bullet pierced his brave young heart from the pistol of Fitzroy
And that was how they captured the Wild Colonial Boy.

The Wild Rover

I've played the wild rover for many a year
And I spent all my money on whiskey and beer,
And now I'm returning with gold in great store
And I never will play the wild rover no more.
Chorus:

And it's no, nay, never,
No nay never no more,
Will I play the wild rover
No never, no more.

I went to an ale-house I used to frequent
And I told the landlady my money was spent.
I asked her for credit, she answered me "nay
Such custom as yours I could have any day."

I took from my pocket ten sovereigns bright
And the landlady's eyes opened wide with delight.
She said "I have whiskey and wines of the best
Sure the words that I spoke, they were only in jest."
I went to my parents, confessed what I'd done
And I asked them to pardon their prodigal son.
They kissed me, caressed me, as oft times before
And never will I play the wild rover no more.

The Wild West Show

Chorus:

We're off to see the Wild West Show,

The elephant and the kangaroo-o-oo,
No matter what the weather, as long as we're together,
We're off to see the Wild West Show.

(Take turns leading verses)
Leader: Now here, ladies and gentlemen, in the first cage we have the laughing hyena.
Pack: The laughing hyena? Fantastic! Incredible! Tell us about the motherfucker!
Leader: This animal lives up in the mountains and once every year he comes down to eat. Once every two years he comes down to drink, and once every three years he comes down for sexual intercourse. What the hell he has to laugh about I don't know.

The Giraffe--This creature is the most popular animal in the animal kingdom. Why? Every time he goes into a bar he says, "Gentlemen, the high-balls are on me."

The Famous Tattooed Lady--On the inside of her left thigh she has tattooed MERRY CHRISTMAS, and on the inside of her right thigh she has tattooed HAPPY NEW YEAR, and she'd like to invite you to come up between the holidays!

The Orangutan--This animal lives in the deepest jungle, and his scrotal sac is so pliant and flexible that as he swings from branch to branch his balls go ORANG-U-TANG, ORANG-U-TANG.

The Rhino-sauras--This animal, ladies and gentlemen, is reputed to be the richest in the world. Its name is derived from the Latin "rhino" meaning money, and "sore ass" meaning piles; hence, piles of money.

The Keerie Bird--This bird lives only in the Antarctic, and every time it lands on the ice it says, "Keerie, Keerie, Keeriest, it's cold!"

The Leo-pard--Yes, folks, the leopard has one spot on its coat for every day of the year. What about leap year? Jim, lift up the leopard's tail and show the lady the 29th of February.

The Winky Wanky Bird--Folks, by some mystery of nature, the nerves of this bird's eyelids are connected to its scrotum. Every time it winks, it wanks, and every time it wanks, it winks. Hey you, boy, stop throwing sand in the bird's eye!

The Mathematical Impossibility--Yes, ladies and gentlemen, the girl you see before you in this cage was ate before she was seven!

The Oozle Woozle Bird--These birds fly in a line ahead formation, and at the first sign of danger, the last bird flies up the asshole of the bird in front, and so on up the line. The remaining bird then flies around in ever-decreasing circles, finally disappearing up its own fundamental orifice, from which it proceeds to shower shit and derision in all directions.

The Second Tattooed Lady--On one leg she has tattooed FIRE, and on the other leg she had tattooed BRIMSTONE, and in between it looks like HELL!

The Gay-zelle--This pretty little four-footed animal you see on your right, ladies and gentlemen, wot has the peculiarity that every time it leaps from rock to rock it farts, and the scientists are still trying to determine whether it farts because it leaps or whether it leaps because it farts.

The Well-Known Oolie-Goolie Bird--This bird, wot as you will observe if you look carefullyt, has no legs, and is called what it is because when the male of the species comes in to land you can hear him cry, "Ooh, me goolies! Ooh, me goolies!"

The French Pervertable--This fine automobile is the last of it's kind, no longer for sale anywhere in the world. Notice the convertible top, the five-speed manual transmission, the automatic cruise control, and the dual halogen headlights. It seats two in the front and comfortably accomodates 69 in the back.

The Tattooed Cowgirl--The tattooed cowgirl has a tattoo of Roy Clark on her left thigh and a tattoo of Hank Williams on her right thigh . . . and who's that in the middle, Willy Nelson?

The Antique Sales Lady--The Antique Sales Lady sells only period furniture . . . everything has stains on it.

The Circus Acrobat--If you will but observe the Circus Acrobat's ass you will observe a tattooed M on one cheek and a corresponding M on the other. When he bends over he spells MOM. When he stands on his head he spells WOW. When he turns cartwheels, he spells WOW MOM WOW.

The Female Mathematician--This lady, folks, believes that this (hold fingers three inches apart) is twelve inches.

The Famous Oooh-Aaah Bird--The male of this species, ladies and gentlemen, resides at the North Pole while the female resides at the South Pole. At the appointed season the male Oooh-Aaah flies south from the North Pole and the female Oooh-Aaah flies north from the South Pole until they meet at the Equator, whereupon one can hear them call, "Oooooooooh-Aaaaaaaaah!"

The Tri-Angular Iceberg--A most uncommon iceberg, ladies and gentlemen, where on the first side you will see an Indonesian keeping a private school, and on the second side an American keeping a private school, while on the third side you will observe a polar bear sliding up and down, keeping his privates cool.

The Homosexual Sparrow--This bird is so called, ladies and gentlemen, because sometimes he flies backwards for a lark.

The Infamous Fuccari Tribe--This tribe, as you will see, dear friends, is composed of small-statured people wot live in the middle of Africa, where the grass grows to an incredible height of 18 feet or more, and all day long the members of this tribe wander, calling, "Where the Fuccari? Where the Fuccari?"

The Fight Between the Snake and the Ostrich (Please note that this one is limited only by the teller's imagination and the audience's patience. So far the Guinness Book of Records has refused to list the longest known version, but a respectable average would be around 15 minutes. What follows is a bare outline; embellish it as you will): In the left-hand corner, ladies and gentlemen, stands the ostrich (to be followed by a life history of the contestant, fight record, size of jock strap, etc.), while in the right-hand corner stands the snake (ditto). And there, ladies and gentlemen, goes the bell for round one (followed by a description of the fight--this round, and all subsequent rounds, should take at least three minutes of fast talking, and should all end in the same way with the snake diving into the ostrich's mouth, wriggling swiftly through the ostrich's digestive apparatus, and emerging from it's asshole. Because of this clever maneuver, each round goes to the snake, until the FINAL round, wherein the snake finally dives into the ostrich's mouth, swiftly wriggles through the ostrich's digestive apparatus, and is ABOUT to emerge from its asshole when the ostrich shoves its beak up its own asshole and says, "Now loop-the-loop, you bastard!").

Three German Soldiers crossed the Line

Tune: When Johnny comes marching home

Three German soldiers crossed the line taboo taboo
Three German soldiers crossed the line taboo taboo

Three German soldiers crossed the line they raped the women and drank the wine and they all said zeig heil tickle my ass taboo.

They came upon a way side inn taboo taboo
They came upon a way side inn taboo taboo
They came upon a way side inn the door was locked so they kicked it in
and they all said zeig heil tickle my ass taboo.

The inn keeper had a daughter fair taboo taboo
The inn keeper had a daughter fair taboo taboo
The inn keeper had a daughter fair With long blond hair And Tits to
There
and they all said zeig heil tickle my ass taboo.

They tied her to a feather bed taboo taboo
They tied her to a feather bed taboo taboo
They tied her to a feather bed and fucked till she was almost dead
and they all said zeig heil tickle my ass taboo.

The inn keeper was so ashamed taboo taboo
The inn keeper was so ashamed taboo taboo
The inn keeper was so ashamed he fucked her back to life again
and they all said zeig heil tickle my ass taboo.

The inn keeper had a trusty gun taboo taboo
The inn keeper had a trusty gun taboo taboo
The inn keeper had a trusty gun he shot the fuckers one by one
and they all said zeig heil tickle my ass taboo.

Three German soldiers marched to hell taboo taboo
Three German soldiers marched to hell taboo taboo
Three German soldiers marched to hell they fucked the devil and his
wife as well and they all said zeig heil tickle my ass taboo.

The moral of the story is taboo taboo
The moral of the story is taboo taboo
The moral of the story is you never fuck in a feather bed
and they all said zeig heil tickle my ass taboo.

The moral of the moral is taboo taboo
The moral of the moral is taboo taboo
The moral of the moral is you always fuck in a water bed
and they all said zeig heil tickle my ass taboo.

The Germans thought they won the war taboo taboo
The Germans thought they won the war taboo taboo

The Germans thought they won the war the newfies won it the day before
and they all said zeig heil tickle my ass taboo.

And they all said zeig heil tickle my ass taboo

The Wreck Of The John B.

Tune: a.k.a. Sloop John B

We come on the sloop John B
My grandfather and me,
'Round Nassau town we did roam.
Drinking all night, got into a fight
I feel so broke up, I want to go home

Chorus:

So hoist up the John B's sail
See how the mains'l's set,
Send for the captain ashore,
To let me go home
Let me go home
I want to me go home
Well, I feel so broke up
I want to go home.

The first mate he got drunk,
Broke up the people's trunk
The constable had to come and take him away,
Sheriff Johnstone, please let me alone
I feel so broke up, I want to go home.

The poor cook he caught the fits
And threw away all of my grits
And then he went and ate up all of my corn.
Let me go home,
I want to go home,
Well I feel so broke up, I want to go home.

The stewardess she got stewed
Ran 'round the poop deck nude
Constable had to come and take her away
Sheriff Johnstone please let me alone
I feel so broke up, I want to go home.

They're Moving Father's Grave

Tune: I Wish I Were an Oscar-Meyer Weiner

They're moving father's grave to build a sewer,
They're moving it regardless of expense,
They're moving his remains to lay down shithouse drains,
To satisfy some nearby residents.

Now, what's the use of having a religion?
For when you die your troubles never cease,
When some high-society twit needs a pipeline for his shit,
They won't let poor father rest in peace.

My father in his life was ne'er a quitter,
I'm sure that he'll not be a quitter now,
He'll put on a white sheet and haunt the shithouse seat,
And he'll only let them shit when he'll allow.

Oh, won't there be some pains of constipation!
And won't those shithouse bastards rant and rave!
But they'll get what they deserve, for they had the bloody nerve,
To bugger up a British workman's grave.

Three Jolly Coachmen (Come landlord fill the flowing bowl)

Three jolly coachmen sat in an English tavern,
Three jolly coachmen sat in an English tavern,
And they decided,
And they decided,
And they decided,
To have another flagon.

Chorus:

Come landlord fill the flowing bowl until it doth run over
Come landlord fill the flowing bowl until it doth run over
For tonight we'll merry merry be,
For tonight we'll merry merry be,
For tonight we'll merry merry be,
Tomorrow we'll be sober.

Here's to the man drinks water pure and goes to bed quite sober.
Here's to the man drinks water pure and goes to bed quite sober.

Falls as the leaves do fall,
Falls as the leaves do fall,
Falls as the leaves do fall,
He'll be dead by next October.

Here's to the man who drinks strong ale and goes to bed quite mellow.
Here's to the man who drinks strong ale and goes to bed quite mellow.
Lives as he ought to live,
Lives as he ought to live,
Lives as he ought to live,
And dies a jolly good fellow.

Now here's to the maid who steals a kiss and runs to tell her mother.
Now here's to the maid who steals a kiss and runs to tell her mother.
She's a foolish, foolish thing,
She's a foolish, foolish thing,
She's a foolish, foolish thing,
She'll never get another.

Now here's to the maid who steals a kiss and runs back for another.
Now here's to the maid who steals a kiss and runs back for another.
She's a boon to all mankind,
She's a boon to all mankind,
She's a boon to all mankind,
She'll very soon be a mother.

Throw A Nickel On The Grass (Vietnam version)

We were cruising over Hanoi, doin' four and fifty per,
When I called to my flight leader, "Oh, won't you save me, sir?
The SAMs are hot and heavy, the MiGs are on our ass,
Take us home, flight leader, please don't make another pass!"

Chorus:

Hallelujah, hallelujah,
Throw a nickel on the grass,
Save a fighter pilot's ass.
Hallelujah, hallelujah,
Throw a nickel on the grass,
And you'll be saved.

I rolled into my bomb run, trying to set the pipper right,
When a SAM came off the launch pad, and headed for our flight.
Then number two informed me, "Hey, four, you better break!"

I racked that Goddamned plane so hard, it made the whole thing shake.

I started my recovery, it seemed that things would be all right,
When I felt the damnedest impact, saw a blinding flash of light.
We held the stick with all our might, against the binding force,
Then number two screamed out at us, "Hey, four, you've had the course!"

I screamed at my back seater, "We'd better punch on out,
Eject! Eject! You stupid shit!" in panic I did shout.
I didn't wait around to see if Joe had got the word,
I reached between my legs and pulled, and took off like a bird.

As I descended in my chute, my thoughts were rather grim,
Rather than be a prisoner, I'd fight them to the end.
I hit the ground and staggered up, and looked around to see,
And there in blazing neon, Hanoi Hilton welcomed me.

Slowly: The moral of this story is, when you're in Package Six,
You'd better Goddamn look around, or you'll be in my fix.
I'm here at Hanoi Hilton, with luxury sublime,
The only thing that's not so greatùI'll be here a long, long, long time.

Traditional Irish Folk Song

They come over here and they take all our land
They chop off our heads and they boil them in oil
Our children are leaving and we have no heads
We drink and we sing and we drink and we die

We have no heads,
No we have no heads

They come over here and they chop off our legs
They cut off our hands and put nails in our eyes
O'Grady is dead and O'Hanrahan's gone
We drink and we die and continue to drink

O'Hanrahan
No O'Hanrahan

They buried O'Neill down in country Shillhame
The poor children crying and fe dee din de
Hin fle di dinfle di din fle de din de

In hey bibble bibble hey bibble bibble

O'Hanrahan
No O'Hanrahan

We drink and we sing and we drink and we sing - *Hey!*
We drink and we drive and we puke and we drink - *Hey!*
We drink and we fight and we bleed and we cry - *Hey!*
We puke and we smoke and we drink and we die - *Hey!*

Virgin Sturgeon

(Tune: Reuben, Reuben, I've Been Thinking)

Chorus:

Caviar comes from the virgin sturgeon,
The virgin sturgeon is a very fine fish,
The virgin sturgeon needs no urging,
That's why caviar is my dish.

I gave caviar to my girlfriend,
She's a virgin through and through,
Since I gave my girlfriend caviar,
There ain't nothing she won't do.

I gave caviar to my bow-wow,
All the other doggies looked agog,
He had what those bitches needed,
Wasn't he a lucky dog?

I gave caviar to my grandpa,
Grandpa's age is ninety-three,
Last time that I saw grandpa,
He's chased grandma up a tree.

My father was a lighthouse keeper,
He had caviar for his tea,
He had three children by a mermaid,
Two were kippers, one was me.

Walkin' 'Round In Women's Underwear

Tune: Winter Wonderland

Lacy things the wife is missin',

Didn't ask her permission,
I'm wearin' her clothes, and silk panty hose,
Walkin' 'round in women's underwear.

In the store, there's a teddy
Little straps, like spaghetti
It holds me so tight, like handcuffs at night
Walkin' 'round in women's underwear.

In the office there's a guy named Melvin,
He pretends that I am Murphy Brown,
He'll say are you ready, I'll say whoa man,
Let's wait until the wife is out of town.

Later on, if you wanna,
We can dress like Madonna,
Put on some eye shade and join the parade
Walkin' 'round in women's underwear.
Walkin' 'round in women's underwear.

Walking Down The Canal Street

Walking down Canal Street,
Knocking on every door,
Goddamn sonofabitch,
Couldn't find a whore.

When I finally found a whore,
She was tall and thin,
Goddamn sonofabitch,
Couldn't get it in.

When I finally got it in,
I turned it all about,
Goddamn sonofabitch,
Couldn't get it out.

When I finally got it out,
It was red and sore,
Goddamn sonofabitch,
You should never fuck a whore.

What A Wank

Tune: William Tell Overture

What a wank, what a wank, what a wank, wank, wank,
What a wank, what a wank, what a wank, wank, wank,
What a wank, what a wank, what a wank, wank, wank,
What a wank, what a wank, wank, wank.

What a wank, what a wank, what a wank, wank, wank, wank, wank, wank, wank, wank, wank,
What a wank, what a wank, what a wank, wank, wank, wank, wank, wank wank.
What a wank, what a wank, what a wank, wank, wank,
What a wank, what a wank, what a wank, wank, wank,
What a wank, what a wank, what a wank, wank, wank,
What a wank, what a wank, wank, wank . . .

What Shall We Do With The Drunken Sailor

What shall we do with the drunken sailor,
What shall we do with the drunken sailor,
What shall we do with the drunken sailor,
Early in the morning?

Chorus:

Way, hey, and up she rises,
Way, hey, and up she rises,
Way, hey, and up she rises,
Earlye in the morning.

Put him to bed with the captain's daughter (three times)
Early in the morning.

Hang him by the balls in a running bowline
Early in the morning.

Shave his crotch with a rusty razor
Early in the morning.

Shove a hosepipe up his asshole
Early in the morning.

Tie his prick in a double half-hitch
Early in the morning.

Shave his nuts and half his eyebrows
Early in the morning.

Pull his dick from the Captain's anus
Early in the morning.

Put him in bed with Margaret Thatcher
Early in the morning.

That's what we'll do with the drunken sailor
Early in the morning.

When Lady Jane became A Tart

Tune: Those in Peril on the Sea

It fairly broke the family's heart,
When Lady Jane became a tart,
But blood is blood and race is race,
And so to save the family face,
They bought her an expensive flat,
With "Welcome" written on the mat.

It was not long ere Lady Jane,
Brought her patrician charms to fame,
A clientele of sahibs pukka,
Who regularly came to fuck 'er,
And it was whispered without malice,
She had a client from the Palace.

No one could nestle in her charms,
Unless he wore ancestral arms,
No one to her could gain an entry,
Unless he were of the landed gentry,
And so before sun had set,
She'd worked her way through Sommerset.

When Lady Anne became a whore,
It grieved the family even more,
But they felt they couldn't do the same,
As they had done for Lady Jane,
So they bought her an exclusive beat,
On the shady side of Jermyn Street.

When Lord St. Clancy became a nancy,
It did not please the family's fancy,
And so in order to protect him,
They did inscribe upon his rectum,
"All commoners must now drive steerage,
This fucking hole is reserved for peerage."

Why Was He Born So Beautyful?

Him... Him... Fuck him.
Why was he born so beautiful?
Why was he born at all?
He's no fucking use to anyone.
He's no fucking use at all.
So drink you mother fucker,
Drink you mother fucker
Drink, Drink, Drink!
Why are we waiting?
Why are we waiting?
He must be masturbating.
Oh why, why, why?

Waltzing Matilda

Once a jolly swagman sat beside the billabong,
Under the shade of a coulibah tree,
And he sang as he sat and waited by the billabong
You'll come a-waltzing matilda with me.
Waltzing matilda, waltzing matilda,
You'll come a-waltzing matilda with me.
And he sang as he sait and waited by the billabong,
You'll come a-waltzing matilda with me.

Down came a jumbuck to drink beside the Billabong,
Up jumped the swagman and seized him with glee,
And he sang as he tucked the jumbuck in his tuckerbag,
You'll come a-waltzing matilda with me.
Waltzing matilda, waltzing matilda,
You'll come a-waltzing matilda with me.
And he sang as he tucked the jumbuck in his tuckerbag,
You'll come a-waltzing matilda with me.

Down came the stockman, riding his thoroughbread,

Down came the troopers, one, two, and three,
"Where's the jolly jumbuck you've got in your tuckerbag?"
You'll come a-waltzing matilda with me.
Waltzing matilda, waltzing matilda,
You'll come a-waltzing matilda with me.
"Where's the jolly jumbuck you've got in your tuckerbag?"
You'll come a-waltzing matilda with me.

Up jumped the swagman and plunged into billabong,
"You'll never catch me alive," said he,
And his ghost may be heard as you ride beside the billabong,
You'll come a-waltzing matilda with me.
Waltzing matilda, waltzing matilda,
You'll come a-waltzing matilda with me.
And his ghost may be heard as you ride beside the billabong,
You'll come a-waltzing matilda with me.

Was It You

Was it you that done the pushin'
Left the stains upon the cushion,
Footprints on the dashboard upside down?
Was it you, you sly woodpecker,
Got into my daughter Rebeccer,
'Cause if is was, you'd best be leaving town.

Yes 'twas I that done the pushin'
Left the stains upon the cushion,
Footprints on the dashboard upside down,
But ever since I've had your daughter,
I've had trouble passing water,
So I guess that makes us even, all around!

Waves And Waves

Tune: Both Sides Now

Waves and waves of golden hair,
Her lips so red, her skin so fair,
Her breasts they were a perfect pair,
They took my breath away.
I courted her from week to week,
I held her hand, I kissed her cheek,
No other favors did I seek,

Or try to get my way.

Chorus:

I've humped with her from both sides now,
In and out, up and down,
In all experience I do declare,
I've never seen a tattoo there.

She sat herself upon my knee,
And turning round she said to me,
"I've saved myself for you, you see,
Until our wedding day,
It's only twice I've been untrue,
The Royal Marines they did me screw,
The Yankee navy laid me too,
And had their ends away."

I must admit I've played some tricks,
What's one destroyer full of pricks?
Royal Marines in their kits,
Would surely lose their way,
But like a cad, my chance did seize,
I'd never been between her knees,
And my pure angel just to please,
Upon her back did lay.

Waves and waves of pubic hair,
The cooties crawling everywhere,
The flavored douches sprayed in there,
It's strawberry today,
And if you get inside her pants,
Cave paintings in the south of France,
The only way that I could chance,
Describing what I saw.

Orangutans hang from her clit,
A serpent's head peers from the slit,
A dragon rampant on each tit,
Each face a different way.
To drop your head and taste the dew,
Is like feeding time at London Zoo,
I took some snake bite serum too,
I'm not ashamed to say.

Now hordes and hordes of curious guys,
Pay for the pleasure and surprise,

Of gazing between my girlfriend's thighs,
It's made me rich today.
So pay me if you feel the need,
No clap, no VD, guaranteed,
Maybe some babies, I'll concede,
Just form a queue--this way.

We Don't Know How Lucky We Are

I was speaking to a mate of mine
Just the other day
A guy called Bruce Bayliss actually,
Who lives up our way
He's been living in Europe
For a year, more a less,
I said "How was Europe, Bruce?"
He says, "Fred, it's a mess."

Chorus:

We don't know how lucky we are, mate,
We don't know how lucky we are.

Me stock agent's got a beach place
Where he spends most of his days;
His wife bit the dust down there last year,
Got eaten by a couple of crays,
And his two littlest daughters
Got killed by a whale.
I said "Are you going down there this year, mate?"
He says "Fred, right on the nail."

So if things are looking really bad
You're thinking of givin' it away
Remember New Zealand's a cracker
And I reckon come what may
If things get appallingly bad
And we all get atrociously poor
If we stand in the queue with our hats on
We can borrow a few million more.

When The End Of The Month Rolls Around

Tune: As the Cassions Go Rolling Along

You can tell by the stain that she's in a lot of pain
When the end of the month rolls around.
You can tell by her stance she's got cotton in her pants
When the end of the month rolls around.

Chorus:

For it's hi, hi, hee, in the Kotex industry,
Shout out your sizes loud and strong (Junior, Regular, Super-Duper, Bale of Hay!)
For wherever you go, you will always know
When the end of the month rolls around.

You can tell by her walk that you'll sit around and talk
When the end of the month rolls around.
You can tell by the blotch that she's got a leaky crotch
When the end of the month rolls around.

You can tell by her eyes that there's blood between her thighs
When the end of the month rolls around.
You can tell by her pout that her eggs are falling out
When the end of the month rolls around.

Wonderful World

Don't know much about Bosnia,
Don't know much about Albania,
Don't know much about Kosovo,
Don't know what an ATM is for,
But I do know, my tour is through,
And I know when I escape this zoo,
What a wonderful world it will be.
Don't know much about protocol,
Never cared about that crap at all,
All these forms begin to look the same,
And I still mispell the boss' name,
But I do know, I'm outta here,
So I'm gonna drink a keg of beer,
And what a wonderful world it will be.

Now I don't claim to be a warfighter
And I don't want to be

'Cause maybe if I was a warfighter baby
They'll expect results from me

Don't know much about Union Flash,
Don't know how I seem to spend my cash,
Don't care much about formality,
Lost my grip upon reality,
But I do know, that life is fine,
When the Freedom Bird lifts off on time,
What a wonderful world it will be.

Sha la la la la la la... *PfP*
Oooooooooohhhhhh... *R.O.E.*
La la la la la la laaaaaaaa... *Island Thunder*
Oooooooooohhhhhh... *O'Grady's Blunder*

But I do know that I'm so short,
you'll have to dig a hole to blow me, sport,
and what a wonderful world it will be.

Whiskey In The Jar

As I was going over the Cork and Kerry Mountains
I met with Captain Farrell, and his money he was countin'.
I first produced my, and then produced my rapier,
Saying "Stand and deliver, for you are a bold deceiver."

Chorus:

Musha ring dumma do dumma da,
Whack for the daddy ol,
Whack for the daddy ol,
There's whiskey in the jar.

I counted out his money, it made a pretty penny,
So I put it in my pocket, and I took it home to Jenny.
She sighed and she swore that she never would betray me,
The devil take those women, for they never can be easy.

I went into my chamber, for to take a slumber,
I dreamt of golden jewels, and sure it was no wonder
That Jenny drew my charges and she filled them full of water
And sent for Captain Farrell to be ready for the slaughter.

It was early in the morning, before I rose to travel,

the guards were all around me, and likewise Captain Farrell.
I then produced my pistol, she had stolen away my rapier,
I couldn't shoot the water, so a prisoner I was taken.

If anyone can save me, 'tis my brother in the army,
If I can find his station in Cork or in Killarney.
And if he'll come and save me, we'll go roving near Kilkenny,
And sure he'd treat me better than me darling sportling Jenny.

Would You Like To Sit On My Face?

Would you like to sit on my face?
Spread your ass all over the place.
Stick my nose in a fragrant place.
Or would you rather suck my log?

Yankee Air Pirate

I am a Yankee air pirate,
With DTs and blood-shot eyeballs,
My nerves are all run down from bombing downtown,
From SAM breaks and bad bandit calls.

Chorus:

> *A Yankee air pirate, a Yankee air pirate, a Yankee air pirate am I,*
> *A Yankee air pirate, a Yankee air pirate, if I don't get my hundred I'll die.*

I've carried iron bombs on the outboards,
Flown fast CAP for F-One-Oh-Thuds,
I've sniveled a counter or two once or twice,
And sweated my own rich red blood.

I've been downtown to both bridges,
To that Nguyen, Dep, and Phuc Yen,
And if you ask me, then I'm sure you can see,
There's no place up there I ain't been.

Yankee Doodle

Tune: I'm a Yankee Doodle Dandy

I'm a Yankee Doodle dandy,

Yankee Doodle do or die,
A real live asshole from the USA,
Drunk every Fourth of July.

Yank my doodle, it's a dandy,
Yankee Doodle zip your fly,
Yankee Doodle limped to London,
Wanking off his pony,
I am that Yankee Doodle guy.

Yogi Bear Song

Tune: Camptown Races

(Take turns leading verses)
There is a bear in the deep dark woods,
Yogi, Yogi,
There is a bear in the deep dark woods,
Yogi, Yogi Bear.

Chorus:

> *Yogi, Yogi Bear,*
> *Yogi, Yogi Bear,*
> *There is a bear in the deep dark woods,*
> *Yogi, Yogi Bear.*

Yogi has a little friend, Boo-Boo, Boo-Boo

Boo-Boo has a girlfriend, Cyndi, Cyndi

Yogi has a girlfriend, Suzi, Suzi

Cyndi has a shaven snatch, Grizzly, Grizzly

Cyndi wears crotchless undies, Teddy, Teddy

Cyndi likes it on the ice, Polar, Polar

Cyndi gets what she deserves, Pregnant, Pregnant

Suzi's boyfriend has no teeth, Gummi, Gummi

Suzi's snatch it smells like cheese, Camel, Camel

Suzi gets four bits an hour, Jingle, Jingle

Cyndi's tampon has no string, Cotton, Cotton

Yogi didn't use a condom, Daddy, Daddy

Boo-Boo likes it upside down, Koala, Koala

Boo-Boo has a twelve-inch cock, Cindy's a lucky bear

Boo-Boo's only three feet tall, Yogi's a lucky bear

Boo-Boo likes it up the butt, Yogi's a lucky bear

Yogi didn't wipe his butt, Brown, Brown

Yogi got a case of crabs, Itchy, Itchy

Boo-Boo likes to stroke his tool, Wanker, Wanker

Yogi also likes young boys, Poofter, Poofter.

YO-HO (WSO's Lament)

Tune: When Johnny Comes Marching Home Again

Oh, gather around and I'll tell you a tale, YO-HO, YO-HO,
Oh, gather around and I'll tell you a tale, YO-HO, YO-HO,
Oh, gather around and I'll tell you a tale,
about a girl we did from Yale,
Get it in, get it out, quick fucking about,
YO-HO, YO-HO, YO-HO!

I put my hand upon her toe, YO-HO, YO-HO,
I put my hand upon her toe, YO-HO, YO-HO,
I put my hand upon her toe, she said,
"Hey WSO, You're way to fucking low!"
Get it in, get it out, quick fucking about,
YO-HO, YO-HO, YO-HO!

I put my hand upon her shin, YO-HO, YO-HO,
I put my hand upon her shin, YO-HO, YO-HO,
I put my hand upon her shin, she said,
"Hey WSO you're making me grin!"
Get it in, get it out, quick fucking about,
YO-HO, YO-HO, YO-HO!

I put my hand upon her calf, YO-HO, YO-HO,
I put my hand upon her calf, YO-HO, YO-HO,
I put my hand upon her calf, she said,
"Hey WSO, you're making me laugh!"
Get it in, get it out, quick fucking about,
YO-HO, YO-HO, YO-HO!

I put my hand upon her knee, YO-HO, YO-HO,
I put my hand upon her knee, YO-HO, YO-HO,
I put my hand upon her knee, she said,
"Hey WSO, you're teasing me!"
Get it in, get it out, quick fucking about,
YO-HO, YO-HO, YO-HO!

I put my cock into her mouth, YO-HO, YO-HO,
I put my cock into her mouth, YO-HO, YO-HO,
I put my cock into her mouth, she said,
"AAAAAUGH, MMMMMPH, THHHPT!"
Get it in, get it out, quick fucking about,
YO-HO, YO-HO, YO-HO!

I put my hand upon her tit, YO-HO, YO-HO,
I put my hand upon her tit, YO-HO, YO-HO,
I put my hand upon her tit, she said,
"Hey WSO, you're squeezin' it!"
Get it in, get it out, quick fucking about,
YO-HO, YO-HO, YO-HO!

I put my hand upon her twat, YO-HO, YO-HO,
I put my hand upon her twat, YO-HO, YO-HO,
I put my hand upon her twat, she said,
"Hey WSO, you're makin' me hot!"
Get it in, get it out, quick fucking about,
YO-HO, YO-HO, YO-HO!

I put my hand upon her clit, YO-HO, YO-HO,
I put my hand upon her clit, YO-HO, YO-HO,
I put my hand upon her clit, she said,
"Hey WSO, you finally found it!"
Get it in, get it out, quick fucking about,
YO-HO, YO-HO, YO-HO!

I put my cock into her butt, YO-HO, YO-HO,
I put my cock into her butt, YO-HO, YO-HO,
I put my cock into her butt, she said,
"Hey WSO, you know I'm a slut!"

Get it in, get it out, quick fucking about,
YO-HO, YO-HO, YO-HO!

Oh, now she lies in a pinewood box, YO-HO, YO-HO,
Oh, now she lies in a pinewood box, YO-HO, YO-HO,
Oh, now she lies in a pinewood box, from sucking
To many WSO COCKS!!!!
Get it in, get it out, quick fucking about,
YO-HO, YO-HO, YO-HO!

We dig her up every now and again, YO-HO, YO-HO,
We dig her up every now and again, YO-HO, YO-HO,
We dig her up every now and again, she did
Us before and she'll do us again!!!
Get it in, get it out, quick fucking about,
YO-HO, YO-HO, YO-HO!

We dig her up every once in a while, YO-HO, YO-HO,
We dig her up every once in a while, YO-HO, YO-HO,
We dig her up every once in a while, to get a good
Look at her vertical smile!
Get it in, get it out, quick fucking about,
YO-HO, YO-HO, YO-HO!

Oh, now she lies in a refrigerator, YO-HO, YO-HO,
Oh, now she lies in a refrigerator, YO-HO, YO-HO,
Oh, now she lies in a refrigerator,
____________fucked her, and ____________ ate her!!!!

I put my hand upon her thigh, YO-HO, YO-HO,
I put my hand upon her thigh, YO-HO, YO-HO,
I put my hand upon her thigh, she said,
"Hey WSO, you're making me high!"
Get it in, get it out, quick fucking about,
YO-HO, YO-HO, YO-HO!

I put my hand upon her zit, YO-HO, YO-HO,
I put my hand upon her zit, YO-HO, YO-HO,
I put my hand upon her zit, she said,
"Hey WSO, that ain't my tit!"
Get it in, get it out, quick fucking about,
YO-HO, YO-HO, YO-HO!

I put my cock into her eye, YO-HO, YO-HO,
I put my cock into her eye, YO-HO, YO-HO,

I put my cock into her eye, she said,
"Hey WSO, you're way too high!"
Get it in, get it out, quick fucking about,
YO-HO, YO-HO, YO-HO!

I put my cock into her ear, YO-HO, YO-HO,
I put my cock into her ear, YO-HO, YO-HO,
I put my cock into her ear, she said,
"Hey WSO, you're nowhere near!"
Get it in, get it out, quick fucking about,
YO-HO, YO-HO, YO-HO!

I put my cock upon her chin, YO-HO, YO-HO,
I put my cock upon her chin, YO-HO, YO-HO,
I put my cock upon her chin, she said,
"Hey WSO, please stick it in!"
Get it in, get it out, quick fucking about,
YO-HO, YO-HO, YO-HO!

Zack

Oh, my dame is Zack, diddlyac, diddlyac
I'm a necrophiliac, diddlyac, diddlyac
Oh, I fuck dead women, diddlyac, diddlyac
And I fill 'em full of semen, diddlyac, diddlyac

Oh, I get frustrated, diddlyac, diddlyac
When a woman gets cremated, diddlyac, diddlyac
Oh, a burial's a must, diddlyac, diddlyac
'Cause you can't FUCK DUST!!!

Zippidy Do Me

Zippidy do me, zippidy hey,
My oh my, what a marvellous lay,
Show me your nipples, open your legs,
Zippidy do me, zippidy hey!

There's a wet spot on the mattress,
And the fact is not debatable--
Everyone is fornicate-able.

Zippidy do me, zippidy hey,

Oh, my God, what a marvellous lay!
Gallon of jism coming your way,
Wonderful feeling, fuck me today!

A Lightning Flash Production:

Unofficial Fighter Pilots Songbook

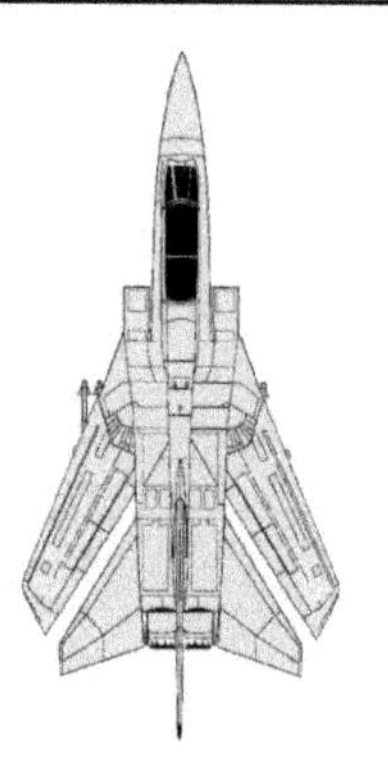

A compilation of songs, poems and quotes from Messes, Officers Clubs and Crewrooms.

1. ***IF I WAS A JAG MATE***
   (Fiddler on the roof)

IF I WAS A JAG MATE
dida dida dida etc
ALL DAY LONG I'D STICK IT UP YOUR BUM
IF I WAS A JAGUAR MAN

I-, WOULDN'T HAVE TO WORK HARD
dida dida etc
ALL DAY LONG I'D STICK IT UP YOUR BUM
IF I WAS A JAGUAR MAN

I'D BUILD A GREAT BIG HOUSE
IN THE MIDDLE OF THE TOWN
FILL IT FULL OF JAG MATES
WITH THEIR TROUSERS DOWN
AND SOME OF THEM WITH NOTHING ON AT ALL

I'D TAKE THEM ALL UPSTAIRS
AND STAND THEM IN A LINE
SOME OF THEM ERECT
ALL ARE LOOKING FINE
AND THEN I'D TAKE THEM ALL
ONE AT A TIME

OOHHHHHHHHH IF I WAS A JAG MATE...... ETC

2. ***SWEET MOLLY MALONE*** ***(trad)***

IN DUBLIN'S FAIR CITY,
WHERE THE GIRLS ARE SO PRETTY,
I FIRST SET MY EYES ON SWEET MOLLY MALONE.
AND SHE WHEELED HER WHEEL BARROW
THROUGH STREETS BROAD AND NARROW
SINGING: (Clap, clap, clap etc)
YOU'RE GONNA GET YOUR FUCKING HEADS KICKED IN.

Fighter Pilots Toasts

Bar R.O.E. (Rules Of Engagment)

The beer light is on at the last day line step, other times with the Sheriff's approval

When deployed, the first Pilot to buy a round of drinks has "the Hammer". The Hammer will only be passed on to the next person who buys another round of drinks. He who possesses the Hammer determines the game of chance played to see who buys the next round.

Presence in the bar is presence in the game.
No hats in the bar.
Sq T-shirts and Friday nametags will be worn on Fridays.
No farting unless first preceded by "Leapord", "Gamecock", "Viper", "Clear", or "No Slugs".
No phone calls from wives in the bar!
No whining!
Don't bring your work into the bar unless it's a gradesheet following debrief.
If you ain't cheatin' you ain't tryin'!
You must have your Squadron coin with you at all times (TDY included)
You must have this Hymnal with you in the bar at all times or have it memorized
It is allowed and highly encouraged to give IQC/MQT/FNG loads of shit for no reason.

A Fighter Pilots Toast

Here's to me in my sober mood,
When I ramble, sit and think,
Here's to me in my drunken mood,
When I gamble, sin and drink.

But when my flying days are over,
And from this world I pass,
I hope they bury me upside down,
So the world can kiss my ass.

Here's to.....

Here's to........, he's true blue,
He's a drunkard through and through,
He's a drunkard so they say,
He wants to go to heaven, but he went the other way.
So drink chug-a-lug, chug-a-lug, chug-a-lug,
So drink chug-a-lug, chug-a-lug, chug-a-lug.
Drink, drink, drink.... [till he's finished his drink]

I'm An Asshole

I'm an asshole, I'm an asshole,
I'm an asshole, yes I am;
But I'd rather be an asshole,
Than to fly the F-16.

A Toast To Those That Fly

We loop in the purple twilight
We spin in the silvery dawn
With black smoke trailing behind us
To show where our comrades have gone

So stand with your glasses steady
This world is a world of lies
We'll drink to those who are living
And hurrah for the next to die.

Various Toasts

Here's to gunpowder and pussy, live by one, die by the other and love the smell of both!

We might not always get what we want, we might not always get what we need, just as long as we don't get what we deserve.

Here's to you... Suckin' My Dick!

Give him a hand, give him a hand, give him a fifth of a hand...FUCK YOU!

Bones heal,
Chics dig scars,
Pain is temporary,
But GLORY is Forever!

Here's to the breezes,
That blows through the treeses,
That lifts the skirts above the kneeses,
That show the spot
That pleases, teases, spreads diseases,
Oh fuck, what a snatch, down the hatch!

A Toast To Honor

Toastmaster: "Let's have a toast to honor."

Response: "Get on her and stay on her!"

Here's To Mag

Here's to Mag, that filthy hag,
That sleazy, slimy slut.
Green fungus lies between her thighs,
And worms crawl out of her butt.

Before I'd scale those scabby legs,
Or suck those pus-filled tits.
I'd drink a cup of buzzard puke,
And die of the grizzly shits!

Other Toasts….

Here's to you and here's to me, may we never disagree,
But if we do, FUCK YOU!, and here's to me.

The Airman's Lament

I am an aviator, I will not drink,
But if I do, I will not get drunk,

But if I do, I will not stagger,
But if I do, I will not fall down,
But if I do, I will fall face first,
so no one can see my wings.

You Cann't Say "Shit Hot"

You can't say "Shit-Hot" in the Officers Club,
You can't say, "Hey, show us your tits!"
The bullshit is getting so deep here, it's up to my fucking armpits.
Fuck off, fuck off, club manager, fuck off, fuck off,
Fuck off, fuck off, club manager, fuck off, fuck off.

Memorandum For Whom It May Concerns

FROM: SAO (Squadron Apology Officer)
SUBJECT: Blanket Apology Letter

Members of the squadron apologize for the following reason:

( ) Missed Flight Records review.
( ) Missed Dental Appointment
( ) Missed Social Disease Clinic.
( ) Missed WG/CC call.
( ) Transmitting on Guard while on a hunting trip.
( ) Missed Chem Warfare Training.
( ) Pissing on the wing sandbags
( ) Hitting the OG/CC's wife with a pool ball.
( ) Saying "Fuck" in the O'Club.
( ) Missed ________________________.
( ) Not letting shoeclerks play Crud on Friday.
( ) Bowling for beer.
( ) Blasting through the Delta Corridor @ FL 190
( ) Walking on parked cars.
( ) Looking up women's dresses while invisible.
( ) Being loud and obnoxious in the Base Theater.
( ) Running over stray cats.
( ) Pissing off the Sky Cops again for _____________.
( ) Pissing off the ADO.
( ) Blanket Apology (to be marked only by Sq Apology Officer) for action in advance of 6 months.

NEIL DOWNENEATER,
Capt, USAF
Acting Squadron Apology Officer

GAMES

OUIJONBU

Description: A game of chance played with 5 dice.
Objective: To win.
Purpose: To promote alcoholism.

BASIC RULES:
The highest total score at the end of the game buys!
Threes count as zero (threes are free) and should be pulled.
Roll all five dice on the first roll.
On each roll, one die is turned over and that point now showing is the point for that roll.
The remaining dice are collected and rolled again.
Again, a die is turned over and that point is added to the growing total.
Repeat five and six until all dice have become points. Total your score and pass the cup.
Remember, because threes are free, they should be pulled prior to turning the point die over. But, if your last die is a three, it must be turned to a four point because of rule #4 in that one dies must be turned over.

COMBAT RULES I:

Violators of these rules buy when "Combat Rules" are in effect:
Each player should pre-flight his ordnance. (If he rolls four instead of five, he buys)
Insulting the dice.
If the value of the dice you select as the point dice is already showing on anther die and you go ahead and turn over the die instead of just pulling the other die, you buy.
Stacking the dice.
Rolling the dice off the bar or table.
Asking what the point is.
The number and buys his friends a round of drinks. If play continues around to the hammer, he must take the next closest number by one.

COMBAT RULES II:

First two or last two is determined prior to pulling the bill out.
The hammer has one look at the bill and places it face down on the table.

The hammer responds either high or low only once for each guess. If he forgets, he buys.
If anyone has to ask what's high or low, he buys but play continues for another round of drinks.
The hammer may claim any number to be the point. (i.e. LIE like a big dog)
If the loser doubts the hammer, he may challenge. If the hammer is in error (i.e. caught lying), the hammer buys. If the kill is validated, the loser buys double.
Anyone guessing outside the high or low bracket buys a round, but the game is continued.

"Deceased Insect"(Dead Bug)

If you don't know how to play "Deceased Insect", ask any BONE DRIVER! Preferably in a crowded room!!!!

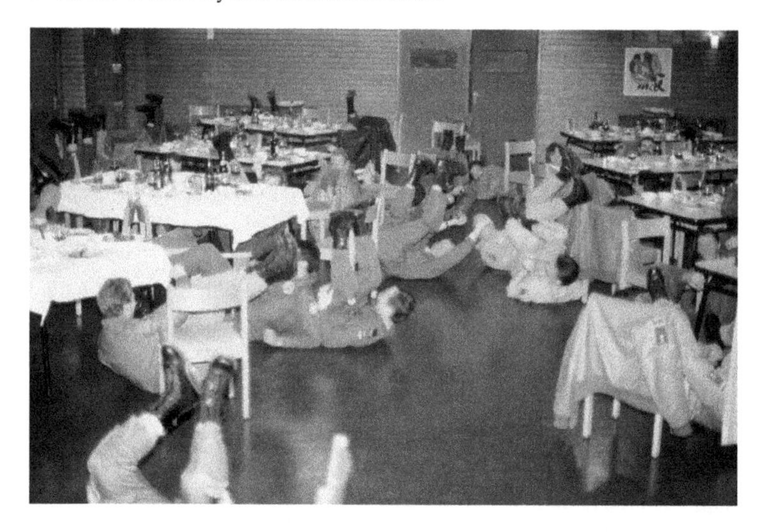

No-Shit Bowling For Beers

(AKA Rolling and Controlling)

Any sub-100 game will result in a beer frame.
Any first ball that is a gutter ball will result in a beer frame.
Any non-mark will result in the next frame being a beer frame.

During a beer frame, it will be the lowest score of both balls (bowling balls) that buys the beer for the beer frame.
If a player drops the gate on a bowler and the bowler's ball strikes the guard, it shall be a beer frame for the guilty bastard that dropped the gate.
There is a three-foot bubble around all bowlers. Violation of this bubble will result in a beer frame for the guilty bastard.
All beer frames will be marked by a star by the bowler's name, and numbered in order. As the beer frames are bought and paid for , the numbers will be circled to indicate payment.
All deliveries of the Mark 3 Mod-00 bowling ball will be restricted to manual deliveries only.
Any complaints that are a direct result of bowling for beer will be farted off. (Unless received by an O-4 or higher, then it will be turned over to the Sq Apology Officer to fart off).
Any change of the ROE or complaints about the ROE will be forwarded to Rick "Rocker Radtke, USAF Ret. or Capt Dan "Moose" Skousen, as they were the founding fathers of bowling for beer. IF these changes or complaints aren't worth a shit, or forwarded along with a case of Pabst Blue Ribbon, don't expect an answer, Fuzz Balls!

21 Aces

A game of chance played with 5 dice and a cup. The player who roles the 21st ACE (one) buys the round. To begin, the player with the hammer rolls all 5 dice. If he rolls one or more Aces, he continues rolling all 5 dice until he doesn't roll any more Aces. He then passes the cup tot he next player. Each player will continue to roll all five dice until the 17th Ace is rolled. Then, only 4 dice are rolled. One more die is removed for each additional Ace rolled, until you have only one die left to roll the 21st Ace.

Majorca 21 Aces

The game is played the same as above except the player who rolls the 7th Ace orders a drink with 4 liquors in it. The player who rolls the 14th Ace pays for the drink. The player who rolls the 21st Ace drinks!

Canadian Rodeo

Find the pretties chick in the bar, go over to her, bite her on the ass, and try to hold on for eight seconds.

Dollar Bill Game

BASIC RULES:

A game of chance played with the serial numbers of any bill denomination (kimchee money is legal), to promote the consumption of any stimulating beverage. The holder of the hammers draws a dollar bill from his wallet. He then asks the smackwad on his left or right to choose first two or last two numbers of the series. Then he asks the person in opposite direction to guess between 0-99. He will state whether that guess was high or low. This is continued until some fool guesses the number and buys his friends a round of drinks. If play continues around to the hammer, he must take the next closest number by one.

COMBAT RULES:

First two or last two is determined prior to pulling the bill out.
The hammer has one look at the bill and places it face down on the table.

The hammer responds either high or low only once for each guess. If he forgets, he buys.
If anyone has to ask what's high or low, he buys but play continues for another round of drinks.
The hammer may claim any number to be the point. (i.e. LIE like a big dog)
If the loser doubts the hammer, he may challenge. If the hammer is in error (i.e. caught lying), the hammer buys. If the kill is validated, the loser buys double.
Anyone guessing outside the high or low bracket buys a round, but the game is continued.

Coin Check

If anyone makes a coin challenge, all crewdogs present must produce their coin within 15 seconds. If one or more people don't have a coin to produce, the coin-less loser(s) must buy everyone a drink of his choice. If all present produce their coin in the allotted time, the challenger buys the round for everyone.

Smiles

You want to know more about the game? Read the book "Fastmovers" by John Darrell Sherwood, Page 103.

STANDARDIZED BREVITY CODES

We are sorely lacking in standardised brevity codes to be used when TDY to an alien O club. The following concise and standardised transmissions may be used by all fighter jocks when manoevering south of the brass footrail:

AUTONOMOUS INTX	MOVING IN ON A CHICK WHILE WEARING A TDY NAMETAG.
BINGO	YOUR BEER CAN'S EMPTY.
BREAK	AGGRESSIVE MANEUVER TO BE USED WHEN YOU'VE GOT A "PIG" AT 6 O'CLOCK AND CLOSING.
BANDIT	UNESCORTED FEMALE.
BUGOUT	LAST DITCH MANOEUVER TO BE USED IF BREAK WAS INEFFECTIVE.
BULLSEYE	THE ONLY FEMALE IN THE BAR.
CHEAP SHOT	A GLASS OF WEED ON THE ROCKS.
CHECK FUEL	SHAKE YOUR BEER CAN.
CONTACT	SHE GAZES UP INTO YOUR EYES.
CONTACT LOST	YOU BREATHED ON HER.
CORNER VELOCITY	THE MAXIMUM SPEED AT WHICH YOU CAN RUN 'EM WITHOUT YOUR GIRL FINDING OUT.
ENGAGED	WHAT SHE THINKS SHE IS IF YOU GIVE HER YOUR SQUADRON PATCH.
FOX 1	THE FIRST GOOD-LOOKING FEMALE IN THE BAR.
FOX 2	THE SECOND GOOD-LOOKING FEMALE IN THE BAR.
FOX 3	N/A AT ACTIVE UNITS.
GRAPE	A BLIND, DEAF, 82 YEAR OLD PARAPALEGIC WHO'S HOT TROT.
IN	ENGAGED FIGHTER IN HOT PURSUIT, IMPLIES THAT FREE FIGHTER EITHER SUPPORT OR GET THE FUCK OUT OF THE WAY.

JINKOUT	REQUIRED MANEUVER WHEN SPOUSE SNEAKS INTO DEEB & UNOBSERVED.
KNOCK IT OFF	CALL MADE BY BANDIT WHEN SHE THINKS THE ENGAEMENT HAS GONE FAR ENOUGH.
SHACK	RESULT OF WELL PLACED KNEE.
ON TGHE DECK	CRAWLING UP TO THE BARSTOOL.
ON TOP	ONE OF TWO CHOICES A BANDIT HAS FOR TERMINATING AN ENGAGEMENT.
PIREP	A LIE JUST TOLD IN THE BAR BY THE JOCK MOST RECENTLY RTB'd FROM TDY.
REATTACK	WHEN YOU ARE UNSACCESSFUL ON YOUR FIRST ATTACK AND THERE'S NOTHING BETTER IN SIGHT.
SCISSORS	A SERIES OF QUICK, CLEVER STATEMENTS DESIGNED TO NEGATE THE BANDIT'S DEFENSIVE MANEUVERING.
SNAP SHOT	"HI, I FLY JETS: HOW YOU IKE IT SO FAR?" (OFTEN FOLLOWED BY KNOCK IT OFF).
ZIPPER	A MAJOR DEFENSIVE THREAT TO AN INEBRIATED FIGHTER JOCK.

Fighter Pilots Party

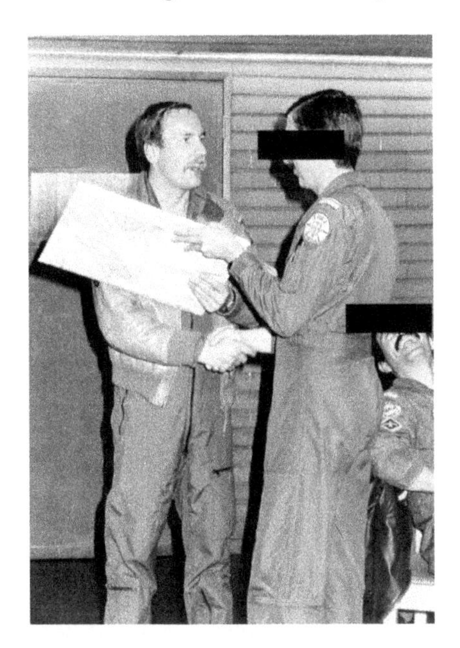

The Party starts with exchanging gifts to the Squadrons.

„Dead Buck“ during the Dinner.

Patrouille with „Pickelhaube“

Fire-Extinguisher

Counteracting steering vehicle.

„Golf“

Fighting with a balloon filled with water.

Ready for ejection.

Ejection game.

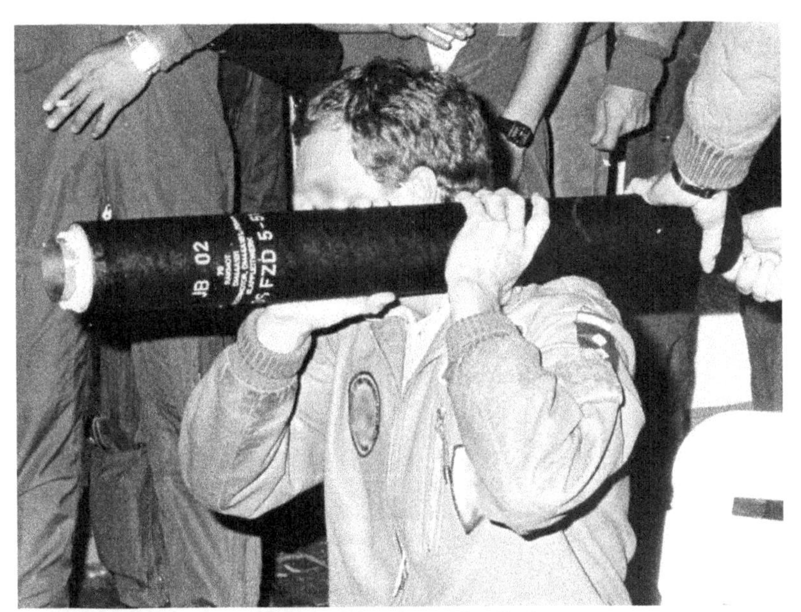

Bazooka Shooting at the Party.

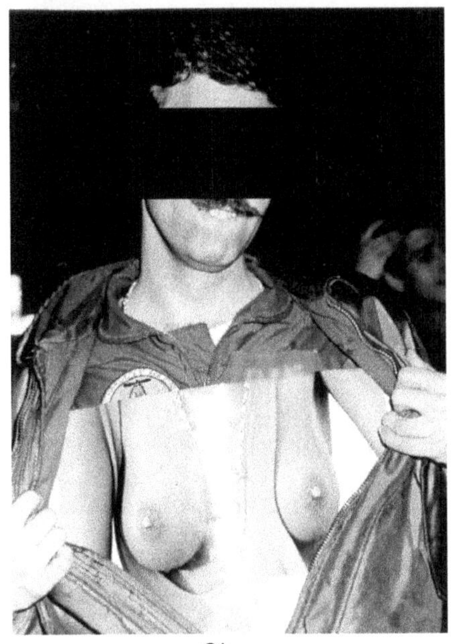

Oh....

„Donkey in the Bar.

Fight is On!

Sources and References

My collection consists of 130+ unpublished Squadron and Wing Songbooks. Few songbooks are from the Army Aviation, some are from the Navy Aviation. Most of the unpublished Songbooks are from Squadrons of the US Air Force, Royal Air Force or German Air Force.
But all of the flyers loved to sing after duty, after a flight, regardless if it was a training flight or a "Hot Mission" and they bombed or gunned somebody on the ground or in the air. Singing and some beer were the pressure relief valve.

For the classic Fighter Pilot song lyrics, refer to the following books:

The Wild Blue Yonder, by C.W. "Bill" Getz, 1981,
The Wild Blue Yonder Volume II, by C.W. "Bill" Getz, 1986,
Singing the Vietnam Blues, by Joseph F. Tuso, 1990

Title of the unpublished Songbook	**Year**
Tommy's Tunes 1st Ed. R.F.C.	1917
Canfield Collection	1925
Collection of Sea Songs and Ditties	1929
Songs The Squadron taught me	1930
Songbook of the Army Air Corps	1937
Liederbuch der Luftwaffe	1939
If You are re nevous in the Service WAAF	1940
Songbook of the Wild Hares	1942
Air Force Airs	1943

Women Army Corps	1943
Songbook Squadron 4 OCS Squadron	1943
Keesler Field Song Book	1943
Songs that Kearnsmen sing	1943
Lowry Field Song Book	1943
Women Army Corps Songbook	1944
US Navy Acorn Thirty-Four	1945
Mess Songs And Rhymes Of The R.A.A.F. (Australia)	1945
Aloha Jigpoha	1945
Airman's Songbook	1945
The Drunk's Album - RAAF Songbook	1944
100th Tuskegee Air Force	1945
Death Rattlers [Korea: Marine Air Squadron VMP-323 "Death Rattlers."]	1951
The Three Hats	1951
Songbook of the 192nd FS	1954
8th Fighter-Bomber Wing Songbook	1954
Untitled VP-9 Naval Aviator Songbook	1955
Naval Aviator Songbook	1956
Songbook of the 318th FIS - Stovepipe Serenade (1956)	1956
The Songs we Sang (in Vietnam)	1957
Songbook of the 18th FBW Kadena Japan	1957
Songbook of the 317th FIS Aces High	1958
The Fighter Pilot's Hymn Book	1958
Songs of Saigon 1st Edition (Songs that Pacify)	1963
Songs of Saigon 2nd Edition (Songs that Pacify)	1963
Songbook of the 523th TFS	1963
General Bowen Untiteld Songbook	1963
Songs of the Saigon Cosmos Command	1964
571st Aviation Company Saigon	1964
Untitled Songbook Hessle RUFC	1964

121th Aviation Company ? Untitled Songsheets by Bill McG.	1964
Cosmos Command Christmas Carols	1964
The Saber	1964
We are here for Fun with the 4926th	1965
Bull Durham Songs of SAC	1965
We're Here for Fun	1966
12 TAC FTR WG Song Book	1966
Phantom Phlyers Sing Vietnam	1966
48th Assault Helicopter Company	1966
197th Aviation Company Vietnam	1966
Songbook of the 12th TFW Cam Ranh Bay	1966
General Landsdale Folkssongs from Vietnam	1998
Songbook of the 433th TFS Ubon	1966
Phantom Phlyers Sing Vietnam	1966
The Fleet Air Arm Songbook Royal Navy	1966
Barracks Ballads	1966
The Crusader Hymnal	1967
355th TFW Yankee Air Pirate Songbook	1967
Airman's Songbook RAF	1967
Songbook of the VMFA 122 Da Nang	1967
Songbook of the 497th TFS Night Owl Ubon	1967
354th TFW SQN Training Manual	1967
Satan's Angels Songbook	1968
35th Tactical Fighter Wing Songbook (1968 Da Nang) along with Dirty Ditties	1968
101st Airborne Division Songbook Phi Bai Vietnam	1968
121st Aviation Company Tiger Tunes	
Songs of SEA and Other Places, Other Things Del Rio Tx	1968
My Golden Songbook of Warsongs Vietnam	1969
Songbook of the 117th HIMS Qui Nhon Vietnam	1969
Songbook of the 354th TFS	1969

Fuck Communism - No Slack Him Book	1969
Songs of the Saints	1969
Songbook of the Raven FACs Laos	1970
44 TFS Hymnal	1970
Bull Durham Songs of SEA	1970
Untitled Songbook (From Reeves)	1970
Songbook of the Transport Command Cam Ranh Bay	1970
Songbook of the No 77 Squadron RAAF	1970
121 Aviations Company 'Tiger Tunes'	1971
The Downwinds DET WESTPAC	1971
Songs My Mother Taught Me (Revised Edition) 77 Squadron RAAF	1971
Songbook of the VMA 224	1971
The SPUD Hymnal	1971
Songs My Mother Taught Me	1971
The Spud Hymnal	1971
Navy Amphibious Anthology of rare Hymns 3rd Edition	1972
VT4 World Famous Rubber Ducks Hymnal	1971
VMA-224 Songbook USS Coral Sea	1972
Songbook of the VMFA 115 Nam Phong, Thailand	1972
17th Wild Weasel's Songbook	1972
Songs of SEA, Other Places, Other Things with Stag Bar Supplement	1972
Fighter Pilots Song No. 77 SQN	1975
Fighter Pilots Songs	1975
44th TFS Hymnal	1975
Dick Jonas Songbook Vol I	1976
Songbook of the 494th Fighter Squadron -Phantom-	1977
527th Aggressor Song Book	1970
Jerry Smith RAF Songs No 47 Squadron	1970

The Fleet Air Arm Songbook Mk. II, Royal Navy	1979
Songbook of the 18th TFS Eielson AFB Alsaka	1980
The Bronco Book 19 TASS Osan Korea	1980
Complete and Official Unexpergated Roadtrip Songbook	1982
Red River Rats Songbook	1983
18th TFS Blue Fox Song Book	1985
43th TFS Song Book Elemendorf Alaska	1985
44th TFS Bat Songs	1985
136 FIS Song Book Niagara Falls	1988
Army Aviation 161 Helicopter Songbook Australia	unknown
The Raven FAC 1990 Reunion Songbook	1990
The Unofficial Fighter Pilot's Songbook	1990
The Longest Year A Collection of Songs by Advisors and Civilians in the Vietnam War	1990
Songbook of the 7440th TFW Incirlik Turkey	1990
230 Tiger Squadron Songbook	1991
7440th Combat Songbook	1991
335th Fighter Sqdn Songbook [(USAF) - F-15 - Combat Songbook]	1991
Bat Songs 44 TFS	1992
Royal Navel Reserve Air Branch Song Book	1992
The Spud Hymnal	1992
88th „Tacos" FS	1995
Women Air Force Service Pilots Songs	1996
53rd TFS NATO Tigers, Spangdahlem	1996
Songs of the F-15 Reunion	1998
Songbook of the 527th Aggressor SQN Alconbury	1999
Songbook of the 322nd TFS GAF Lechfeld	1999
Songbook Compilation from TLP (Tactical Leadership Program)	2000
TLP (Tactical Leadership Program)Drinking Games	2001

37th BS Bonedriver's Squadron Songbook	2002
400 Squadron Song Book (Canada)	2002
Songbook of the 36th FS (South Korea)	2002
Compilation of Fighter Pilot Songs	2003
37th BS B-1B Song Book (2002)	2002
Songbook of the VMFA 251 K-6 Korea	2004
SPUD Hymnal 131th Danang Vietnam 2nd. Ed.	2004
Untitled Songbook by Mark Thomas	unknown
Untitled Songbook From Rob Willis	unknown

And finally the famous Interview of the Vietnam War Era:

What the Captain means[1]

Interview with a Phantom Pilot...

The following interview was recorded when a civilian correspondent interviewed a shy, unassuming Air Force F-4 Phantom jet pilot. To make sure the true Air Force story was told the wing Information Officer (IO) was on hand. The captain was asked his opinion of the F-4 Phantom.

"It's so fucking maneuverable you can fly up your own asshole with it."

"What the Captain means to say is that he has found the F-4 highly maneuverable at all altitudes and he considers it an excellent aircraft for all missions." said the IO.
"I suppose, captain, that you've flown a number of missions in North Vietnam. What do you think of the SAM missile used by the North Vietnamese ?"

"Why those bastards couldn't hit a bull in the ass with a base fiddle!" Exclaimed the Captain

^^What the Captain means is that the surface to air missiles around Hanoi pose a serious threat to our air operations and that the pilots have a healthy respect for them." said the IO.
"I suppose, Captain that you've flown missions to the south. What kind of ordinance do you use and what kind of targets do you hit?"

"Well, I tell ya, mostly we aim to kicking the shit out of the Vietnamese villages, and my favorite ordinance is napalm, man that stuff just sucks the air right out of their friggin lungs and makes a sun of a bitching fire".

"What the Captain means is that the air strikes in South Vietnam are often
against Viet Cong structures, and that operations are always under the positive control of a forward air controller, or FAC. The ordinance is conventual 500 and 750 pound bombs and 20 mm cannon fire. Said the IO.
"I suppose you went on R&R in Hong Kong, What was your impression of the oriental girls"?
"Yeah I went to Hong Kong, and as far as those oriental broads, well it don't

---

1 SPUD Songbook

matter which way the runway runs, east-west, north-south, a piece of ass is a piece of ass!"

"What the Captain means is that he found the delicately featured oriental girls most fascinating and very impressed with their fine manners, and thinks their naivete most charming." Said the IO.
"Tell me Captain have you flown any missions other than in North and South Vietnam?"

"You bet your sweet ass I've flown other missions than the north and south We get fragged every day for missions in Cambodia and Laos. Those little bastards throw every thing, even the kitchen sink, even the kids have slingshots!"

"What the Captain means is that occasionally he flies missions in the extreme western DMZ, and he has a healthy respect for the FLAK in the area." Said the IO.
"I understand that nobody in the 12th tactical fighter wing has got a MIG.
What seems to be the problem?"

"Why you screwhead, If you knew anything about the problem with MIGs. Those peckerheads at seventh for those encounters in MIG valley, You'd bet your ass we'd get some of those mothers, Those glory hounds at Ubon get all the frags while we got to settle for fighten' the friggin war. Those mothers at Ubon are sittin' on their fat asses killing MIGs while we get stuck bombing those goldarn cabbage patches!"

"What the Captain means is that each element of the seventh airforce is responsible for their assigned job in the air war. Some elements are responsible for neutralizing enemy air strength, while other elements are assigned bombing missions interdicting enemy supply routes." Said the IO.
"Captain of all the targets you've hit in Vietnam, which one was the most satisfying?"

"Well shit I tell you, it was the time i was fragged on a suspected VC vegetable garden. I dropped napalm in the middle of the fucking cabbage and rutabagas and
my wing man splashed it real good with 750 pound mothers and spread the fire all the way to the friggin beets and carrots!"

"What the Captain means is that the great variety of tactical targets available throughout Vietnam make the F-4 the perfect aircraft to provide flexible response to any target." Said the IO.
"What do you consider to be the most difficult target you've struck in North Vietnam?"

"The friggin bridges. I must a dropped forty tons of bombs on those swayin bamboo mothers and I ain't hit one yet."

What the Captain means interdicting bridges along enemy routes is very important and is a quite difficult target. The best way to accomplish this is to crater the approaches to the bridges." Said the IO.
"I've noticed from touring, the various sections of the airfield are covered with aluminum mating and on the taxiways. Would you care to comment
on its usefulness and effectiveness in Vietnam."

"You're fucking right I would like to comment, most of us pilots are well hung, but you don't know what hung up is until get hung up on one of those bumps on the goldurn stuff!"

"What the Captain means is that the aluminum matting is quite satisfactory
as a temporary expedient, but requires some finesse in taxing and braking the aircraft." Said the IO.
"Did you have an opportunity to meet your wife on R&R in Honolulu, and did you enjoy your visit with her?"

"Yeah I met my wife in Honolulu, but I forgot to check the calendar so the whole five days were pretty well combat proof. A complete dry run."

"What the captain means is that it was wonderful to get together with his wife and family and learn first hand how things were going at home." Said the IO.
"Thank you for your time Captain."

"Screw you , why don't you bastards print the real story, instead of that crap!"

"What the Captain means is that he enjoyed the opportunity to discus his tour with you." Said the IO.
"Oh, one final question Captain, could you reduce your impression of the
war into a simple phrase or statement?

"You bet your ass I can, it's a fucked up war!"

"What the captain means is **it's a fucked up war**," said the IO.

The Miserable End.

Milton Keynes UK
Ingram Content Group UK Ltd.
UKHW012007080224
437493UK00013B/363